D1191377

RADIATIONS AND MATTER

RADIATIONS AND MATTER

★

ANDRÉ BERTHELOT

Maître de Conférences, Science Faculty, Paris; Head of the Nuclear Physics Section of the French Atomic Energy Commission

English Translation by

F. R. PAULSEN

B.Sc. (London), Ph.D. (Sheffield), F.R.I.C., F.C.S.

Consultant Editor of *Atomics and Nuclear Energy*

LONDON

LEONARD HILL [BOOKS] LIMITED

EDEN STREET, N.W.1

1958

First published 1958

Translated from the French
Rayonnements de Particules Atomiques,
Électrons et Photons

PRINTED IN GREAT BRITAIN BY
SPOTTISWOODE, BALLANTYNE & CO. LTD.
LONDON AND COLCHESTER

CONTENTS

TRANSLATOR'S NOTE

André Berthelot's *Rayonnements de Particules Atomiques, Electrons et Photons* is, I feel, a book which should be read by all interested, or engaged, in the various fields embraced by the title 'Nuclear Physics'.

It deals with the characteristics of various types of radiations, and their behaviour as they pass through matter. For this reason I have taken the liberty of adopting for this translated version the somewhat shorter title which now appears, and which I sincerely hope will in no way detract from the value of the subject-matter which has been so well presented by the author.

While there is little room today for the purist in this utilitarian world, I feel that scientific terminology should retain enough dignity to allow it to avoid becoming ridiculous. The suffix '-on', used for minute particles such as the electron, neutron, and proton, has unfortunately been made to expand into 'tron', so beloved by Americans, with the result that we get absurdities such as 'mesotron', 'positron', and 'negatron'. Consequently, I have adhered, in this translation, to the French terms such as 'negaton' and 'positon', which are much more justifiable. It would be a good thing if such terms could be universally used for the particles of matter, though it might be convenient to retain the suffix 'tron' for use in the names of machines used for handling such particles, such as exist already in names such as 'cyclotron', 'bevatron', 'sychrotron', and even the 'perhapsotron'.

I trust that readers will not find inconvenience in the liberty I have taken with current usage.

F. R. PAULSEN

BRIGHTON,
May, 1957

Chapter 1

GENERALITIES

(1) Energy Considerations

A corpuscle of mass m (differing from zero), travelling with a velocity of v, possesses, according to classical mechanics, a kinetic energy equal to $\frac{1}{2}mv^2$, while its impetus or momentum is mv. When m and v are both expressed in c.g.s. units, the kinetic energy is in ergs. The erg is a unit inconveniently large for use in corpuscular physics, and it is preferable to make use of a much smaller unit, the electron-volt. The value of this unit is the kinetic energy acquired by an electron accelerated from rest through a potential of 1 volt, and such kinetic energy, in ergs, equals the product of the accelerated charge (in this case, $e = 4 \cdot 80 \times 10^{-10}$ c.g.s. electrostatic units) and the potential difference producing acceleration (in this case, 1 volt or $\frac{1}{300}$ c.g.s. electrostatic unit). Thus, we have

$$1 \text{ electron-volt} = 1 \cdot 60 \times 10^{-12} \text{ erg.}$$

Further, the electron-volt (or ev) is often used in the form of multiples, i.e. kiloelectronvolt (kev), megaelectronvolt (Mev), and gigaelectronvolt (Gev) or billion electronvolt (Bev), which equal $1 \cdot 60 \times 10^{-9}$ erg, $1 \cdot 60 \times 10^{-6}$ erg, and $1 \cdot 60 \times 10^{-3}$ erg, respectively.

Relativity mechanics has shown the equivalence of mass and energy, and we know that the mass m of a corpuscle is just one manifestation of energy, which expressed in ergs equals mc^2, according to the relationships deduced by Einstein. In this expression, c is the velocity of light in cm./sec., this value being $2 \cdot 993 \times 10^{10}$, usually approximated to 3×10^{10}, and m is the mass in grammes. Thus the energy equivalent to a mass of 1 gramme is 9×10^{20} ergs.

But the relativity theory tells us more than this, and it shows that the total energy E associated with a body in motion, i.e. the sum of the energy equivalent to the rest mass and the kinetic energy, is not expressible as

$$E = mc^2 + \tfrac{1}{2}mv^2$$

but by

$$E = \frac{mc^2}{\sqrt{(1-\beta^2)}},$$

where β is v/c, v being the velocity of the particle.

From this formula, we may deduce that the kinetic energy, considered as that part of the total energy associated with the effects of motion, is equal to

$$E_{\text{kin}} = E_{\text{tot}} - mc^2 = mc^2\left(\frac{1}{\sqrt{(1-\beta^2)}} - 1\right).$$

When β is very small compared with unity, i.e. when the velocity of the particle is very small compared with that of light, the fraction in the brackets may be replaced by the first term in the expansion of the series, when we get

$$E_{\text{kin}} = mc^2(\tfrac{1}{2}\beta^2) = \tfrac{1}{2}mv^2,$$

which, of course, is the expression given by classical mechanics. This Newtonian approximation, however, does not become applicable when terms in β^4 are no longer negligible when compared with those in β^2, and in such cases the relativistic formula must be applied.

This means that kinetic energy increases at a rate not proportional to velocity as reckoned by classical mechanics, but more rapidly, and tends asymptotically towards infinity as the velocity approaches the speed of light. As it is physically impossible to impart to material particles, for which m is not equal to zero, an infinite energy, it is impossible also to attain the speed of light. This velocity is a limiting value towards which particle speeds approach as these particles are given higher energies, but which can never actually be attained.

The Table below (*see also* Fig. 1) shows, for different values of β, the total energies of particles, taking as unity the energy corresponding to the mass.

β	$\frac{E}{mc^2} = \frac{1}{\sqrt{(1-\beta^2)}}$	β	$\frac{E}{mc^2} = \frac{1}{\sqrt{(1-\beta^2)}}$
very minute	$1+\frac{1}{2}\beta^2$	0·9	2·29
0·01	$1+(5\times10^{-5})$	0·95	3·20
0·1	$1+(5\times10^{-3})$	0·97	4·11
0·2	1·02	0·99	7·08
0·5	1·15	0·999	22·3
0·8	1·66	$1-\epsilon$	$\frac{1}{\sqrt{(2\epsilon)}}$

The value of m is the rest mass, while the quantity $\mu = m/\sqrt{(1-\beta^2)}$ is the dynamic mass, which increases with velocity, so that the total energy of the particle is always expressible by $E = \mu c^2$.

Similar considerations apply to momentum, which in the mechanics of relativity is represented by the vector $\vec{P} = \mu\vec{v} = m\vec{v}/\sqrt{(1-\beta^2)}$. By the application of the Newtonian approximation, this becomes the classical vector $\vec{P} = m\vec{v}$.

Corpuscles travelling with the speed of light are the photons, which are the constituent tiny units of electromagnetic field of which light is but one manifestation, while radio waves, X-rays, and γ-rays are other types, differing only in their wavelength λ (or their frequency ν,

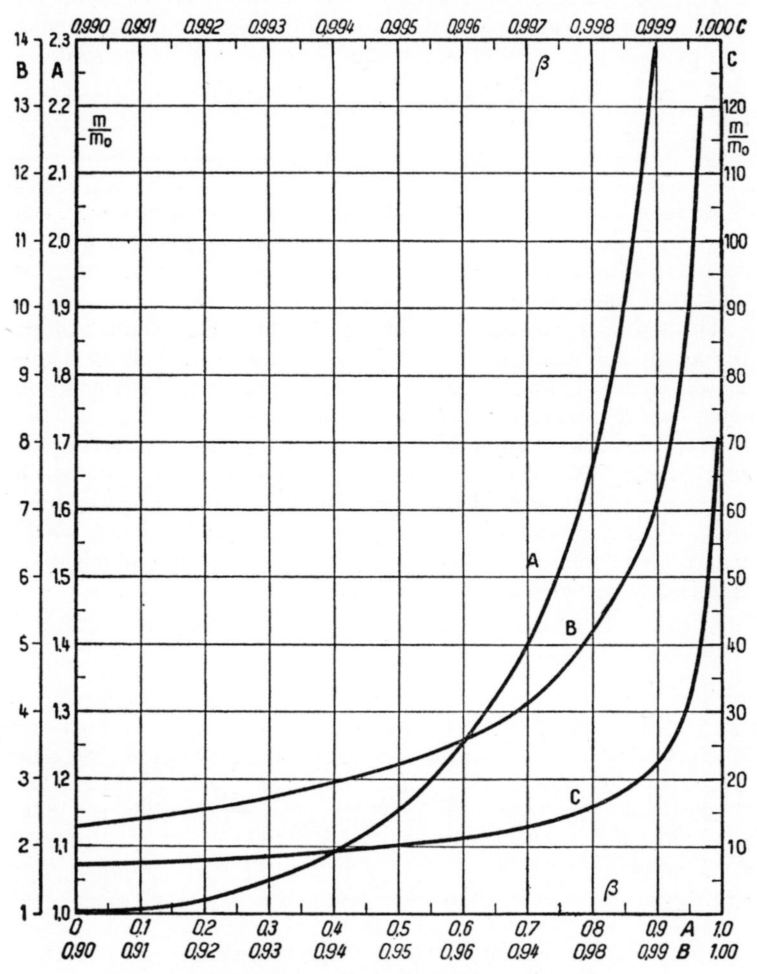

FIG. 1.—Variation of dynamic mass with particle velocity.

equal to c/λ). A photon carries an energy E, related to the frequency by the Planck-Einstein equation $E = h\nu$, where, if E and ν are in c.g.s. units, the h has a value of $6 \cdot 625 \times 10^{-27}$ erg sec., and is known as Planck's constant.

The existence of particles of finite energy, but with velocity equal to c, cannot be realized, as the relativistic energy formula shows, unless the rest mass is zero. Such a particle can have an energy differing from zero only if the velocity equals c, so that it cannot exist unless it has such a speed. This is the case with the photon, and it seems to apply also to neutrinos emitted during β radioactive decay.

For such particles the impetus is defined by a vector along the direction of propagation, and equal to E/c. For a particle of finite rest mass, the energy and momentum are connected by the relationship $|\vec{P}| = E\beta/c$, which, as β approaches unity, tends towards $|\vec{P}| = E/c$.

(2) Energy Units

Since mass and energy are related, the gramme, as we have seen, can be expressed in terms of ergs, but the value is too great for work in corpuscular physics. Therefore, we make use of a unit which, for want of a better name, we call the mass unit (M.U.).

This unit is one-sixteenth of the mass of the lightest stable isotope of oxygen, and it equals $1{\cdot}66 \times 10^{-24}$ g., or 931 Mev. This mass unit closely approximates to the masses of the proton and the neutron, which are respectively 1·0076 and 1·0090 M.U.

The Table below summarizes the relationships between the various units which have been mentioned, together with a few more which are of use in this work. These units are involved in energy calculations connected with installations such as nuclear reactors, where macroscopic amounts of energy are produced by large numbers of elementary particles.

	1 Mev	1 erg	1 kWh	1 cal	1 M.U.	1 g.
Mev	1	$6{\cdot}25 \times 10^{5}$	$2{\cdot}25 \times 10^{19}$	$2{\cdot}62 \times 10^{13}$	931	$5{\cdot}61 \times 10^{26}$
erg	$1{\cdot}60 \times 10^{-6}$	1	$3{\cdot}60 \times 10^{13}$	$4{\cdot}18 \times 10^{7}$	$1{\cdot}49 \times 10^{-3}$	$9{\cdot}00 \times 10^{20}$
kWh	$4{\cdot}45 \times 10^{-20}$	$2{\cdot}78 \times 10^{-14}$	1	$1{\cdot}16 \times 10^{-6}$	$4{\cdot}14 \times 10^{-17}$	$2{\cdot}5 \times 10^{7}$
cal	$3{\cdot}82 \times 10^{-14}$	$2{\cdot}39 \times 10^{-8}$	$8{\cdot}62 \times 10^{5}$	1	$3{\cdot}56 \times 10^{-11}$	$2{\cdot}15 \times 10^{13}$
M.U.	$1{\cdot}074 \times 10^{-3}$	671	$2{\cdot}42 \times 10^{16}$	$2{\cdot}81 \times 10^{10}$	1	$6{\cdot}02 \times 10^{23}$
g.	$1{\cdot}78 \times 10^{-27}$	$1{\cdot}11 \times 10^{-21}$	$4{\cdot}00 \times 10^{-8}$	$4{\cdot}64 \times 10^{-14}$	$1{\cdot}66 \times 10^{-24}$	1

(3) Principles of Conservation

Among the fundamental principles upon which modern physics is based are two which play an important part in phenomena which are to be described later. These concern the conservation of energy and of momentum.

According to the principle of conservation of energy, the total energy in an isolated system remains constant whatever happens within that system. It must not be forgotten that total energy is concerned here, irrespective of the form that the energy may take, and that energy equivalent to rest mass must be taken into account. In classical mechanics, physics and chemistry, changes in the rest mass, resulting in conversion into energy such as heat or kinetic energy, are considered to involve such small amounts of matter that they may be neglected, and the same applies to the reverse process in which energy is transformed into matter. Thus, one can then consider as separate principles the conservation of energy (mass being neglected) and the conservation of mass (Lavoisier's law). In nuclear physics, however, reciprocal transformations between mass and the other forms of energy are often of great importance, and reach sometimes 0·1 per cent in nuclear reactions, or even 100 per cent in the case of the annihilation of an electron and a positon. In such cases, the two physical conservation laws become merged into a single principle concerned with the various manifestations of energy.

According to the principle of the conservation of momentum, the momentum in an isolated system, defined by the vectorial summation of the momenta of the constitutive particles, remains constant, whatever happens within the system. In the case of particles with velocity which is not negligible when compared with light, then it is the relativistic expression for momentum which must be used.

(4) Binding Energies

When particles are assembled together in a complex system such as a molecule, atom or atomic nucleus, and this system is not undergoing any spontaneous disruption with liberation of one or more constituent particles, the intervention of some external source of energy is necessary in order that separation of the particles shall occur.

For example, the component electrons of an atom do not leave that atom spontaneously, except by the action of some external provocation, a process which is known as ionization. This process is only possible when the energy supplied for the purpose exceeds a certain minimum value. Thus, when the electron of the hydrogen atom is removed, the energy supplied must exceed 13·5 ev. If more than this energy is imparted, then the electron will have left the atom with a kinetic energy equal to the difference between the supplied energy and the 13·5 ev. The energy required for removal of a particle from a complex system in which it is held, without imparting any energy of motion, is called the binding energy.

In the reverse phenomenon, i.e. when a particle with kinetic energy is absorbed into a complex system, the energy liberated will be equal to the binding energy. Thus, if an electron at rest becomes attached to a proton, with formation of a hydrogen atom, there is an emission of energy of 13·5 ev, as a photon.

The binding energies of electrons in atoms are of importance in many phenomena, and it is often useful to carry in one's head a few ideas of their magnitude. Electrons are arranged in atoms in distinct levels, characterized by the fact that those electrons in any one level have all approximately the same binding energies. The levels, arranged in order of increasing energies, are referred to as the K, L, M, ... levels. Each K level cannot hold more than two electrons, the L shell 8, the M shell 18, and so on; in general, this number is given by $2n^2$, where n is the ordinal number of the level, and is known as the principal quantum number.

The binding energy of a K electron increases from 13·5 ev in the case of the hydrogen atom, to 116 kev in the case of uranium. In the L level, which exists only in elements from lithium onwards, the electrons are actually in three sub-levels, referred to as the LI, LII, and LIII respectively, and differing slightly in their binding energies, this difference being only a few mv in the case of lithium, but rising to perhaps 20 kev in the case of uranium. In the M level, which makes its appearance from sodium onwards, there are five sub-levels, in which binding energies range from over several ev in the case of sodium to several kev in the case of heavy atoms.

From the theory of atomic structure, it is deduced that the binding energy, in ev, may be expressed by the equation

$$E = \frac{13 \cdot 5}{n^2}(Z - a_n)^2,$$

where Z is the atomic number of the atom under consideration, n its principal quantum number for the level concerned, and a_n a term which varies with Z, compared with which it is very small. Thus, in the case of the K level, we have

$$E_k = 13 \cdot 5(Z - a_1)^2,$$

a_1 being zero when Z is 1 or 92, and passing through a maximum, equal to 4, in the case of atoms of medium Z value.

Another equation, which is purely empirical, is

$$E_k = 5 \cdot 42 Z^{2 \cdot 2},$$

which gives values correct to within 3 per cent except when Z is 1. In Fig. 2 are given the variations in binding energies for K, L, and M levels, as functions of Z.

In atomic nuclei, composed of protons and neutrons, this conception of binding energies also applies. The theory of nuclear levels is only now taking shape, and experimental results have not yet reached the same degree of accuracy that has been possible in the study of electronic levels. Details that have been worked out will not be considered here, but it may be mentioned that nuclear binding energies are of the order of 6 to 8 Mev per neutron or proton; such values are much greater than those applicable to electrons in atoms. Thus are explained the large energies associated with experiments in nuclear physics, which are frequently of the order of Mev, and often greater.

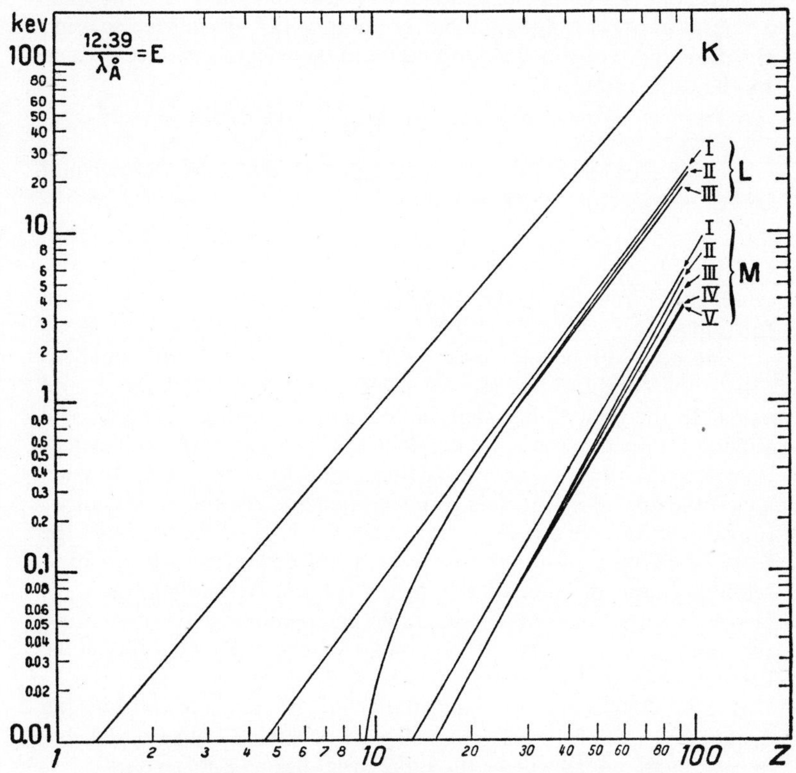

FIG. 2.—Variations in binding energies for K, L, M electrons.

(5) THE CONCEPT OF EFFECTIVE CROSS-SECTION

Imagine a point particle A moving in a medium composed of spherical particles B of radius R, separated from each other by mean distances very much greater than R, and distributed at random with a mean density of n particles per c.c. What is the probability that A will come into contact with a corpuscle of type B?

Consider the medium as divided by two planes P and P^1 perpendicular to the trajectory of A and at a distance dx such that

$$dx \ll \frac{1}{n\pi R^2}.$$

Between these two planes will be ndx particles of type B in each c.c., and if these are projected upon P, they give rise to ndx spots of area πR^2. The condition $n\pi R^2 dx \ll 1$ indicates that the total surface covered by these spots is very small compared with the sq. cm. on which they are projected.

If A, in traversing the distance dx, is to strike a particle B, it must traverse one of the spots forming the projection upon P. As the spots are randomly distributed and cover an area $n\pi R^2 dx$ in each sq. cm., the probability of contact $d\varpi$ is equal to the effective surface divided by the total surface, i.e.

$$d\varpi = n\pi R^2 dx,$$

while the quotient $p = d\varpi/dx$, or the probability of impact per unit length of trajectory, may be written as

$$p = n\sigma,$$

where πR^2 is rewritten as σ, which is called the effective cross-section for impact.

If now we do not consider a thickness dx sufficiently small to satisfy the condition given above, we may take a thickness x and calculate the probability that in traversing the distance x, A will suffer no impact. Let x be divided into k equal parts, sufficiently numerous to allow x/k to satisfy the condition $n\sigma(x/k) \ll 1$. In such a case the preceding formula can be applied, as the probability of no impact within an element of trajectory x/k is $1 - n\sigma(x/k)$, while the total probability of no impact within the distance made up of k sections is the product of the successive relative probabilities, i.e. $[1 - n\sigma(x/k)]^k$. The smaller the individual sections of the trajectory, the more accurate is the formula, and the required probability is the limiting value as k becomes infinite, i.e. $e^{-n\sigma x}$.

If $e^{-n\sigma x}$ represents the probability of no collision within the distance x, the probability of collision occurring between the distances x and $x + dx$ will be the differential $d\varpi_x = e^{-n\sigma x} n\sigma dx$.

By means of this expression the mean free path can be calculated, this is the mean distance travelled before the impact of A upon B, obtained by integrating all the values of x between zero and infinity, with the probability included:

$$\lambda = \int_0^\infty x e^{-n\sigma x} n\sigma dx = \frac{1}{n\sigma}.$$

Such considerations are based upon a model which is only remotely related to conditions met in practice. But they do take into account the essential features and facilitate an understanding of the effective cross-section.

Now consider a particle A moving in a material medium containing n atoms per c.c., and let it be an electrically-charged particle. It will thus be able to remove an electron from any of the atoms in the space traversed if it passes close enough to exert a sufficiently intense electromagnetic field.

If the medium be considered homogeneous, whatever trajectory element of length dx be considered, the probability $d\varpi$ of observing the formation of an ion-pair within this element will be always the same, and proportional to dx as long as this remains minute compared with unity. The quantity $p = d\varpi/dx$ is the probability per unit length of trajectory of the formation of an ion-pair. Arguments similar to those developed above show that the probability that the interval between two creations of ion-pairs lies between x and $x+dx$ is given by the exponential law $pe^{-px}dx$, the mean value of the interval being $\lambda = 1/p$.

In order to evaluate λ we must count the number, ν, of ion-pairs formed along a length, l, of the path, which shall be of suitable length. Then we have

$$\lambda = \frac{l}{\nu} \qquad \text{or} \qquad p = \frac{\nu}{l}.$$

It often happens, in practice, that in place of a single path long enough to involve a great number of collisions, there may be many paths, each of which consists of a very short track in the medium concerned. In this case, out of N trajectories there will be αN, where $\alpha \ll 1$, giving rise to ionization. The α then represents the probability $p\delta$ of the formation of an ion-pair along the track δ, where

$$p = \frac{d}{\delta}.$$

The effective cross-section can always be evaluated from $p = n\sigma$, where n is the number of atoms per c.c. This is justified provided that the probability p is proportional to the concentration of particles of the medium traversed, since the effective cross-section then becomes independent of this concentration and represents a characteristic dimension of the atom.

In particular, it is independent of the state of the medium, whether solid, liquid, or gas. Such a proportionality between p and the concentration is found to apply in practice in the majority of cases, and signifies that the interaction between the corpuscle A and the corpuscle B is unaffected by the proximity of other corpuscles of B. But exceptions do arise, and effective cross-section then varies with concentration. Thus, ionization may be affected, as will be seen later, by polarization, produced only in condensed media. In such cases the effective cross-section of the atoms of the medium varies according to the physical state of the medium. Such cases, nevertheless, are rare.

An effective cross-section can be visualized, defined as above, as an apparent surface σ surrounding each particle of B. Such analogy must not be pushed too far, however. These effective cross-sections are nearly always a function of the speed of the particles of type A, a feature which is incompatible with the purely geometrical conception of the cross-section.

One can also speak of partial effective cross-sections when the phenomenon can be considered as made up of several partial phenomena. Thus, the effective cross-section for ionization, σ, may be the sum of partial cross-sections corresponding to ionizations in the K, L, ... levels, so that

$$\sigma = \sigma_K + \sigma_L + \ldots$$

In general, a phenomenon can be characterized by a dimension which can vary in a continuous fashion and ionization may be associated with the kinetic energy acquired with each electron removed from an atom.

If we consider only electrons removed with kinetic energies between E and $E + \mathrm{d}E$, the differential effective cross-section for these is given by

$$\mathrm{d}\sigma_E = f(E)\mathrm{d}E$$

such that

$$\sigma = \int_0^{E_{max}} f(E)\mathrm{d}E.$$

E_{max} is the maximum kinetic energy which the particle A can give up in a collision with an atomic electron.

Chapter 2

THE THEORY OF ELASTIC COLLISION

(1) Consequences of the Principles of Conservation

Before a study of the behaviour of radiations in matter is possible, we must consider a number of formulæ relating to corpuscular interaction.

Each particle involved in nuclear physics is characterized by the ability to act upon similar, or different, particles with forces which are not appreciable except within a certain space around the particles. These forces are often electrostatic, but may be more complex. This is the case, for example, with those forces which are specifically nuclear.

Whatever the forces involved, the principles of the conservation of energy and momentum must be satisfied, so that the consequences of these principles remain applicable under all circumstances.

Such consequences may now be considered by studying the disturbance created by the passage of one particle through the field of force of another particle.

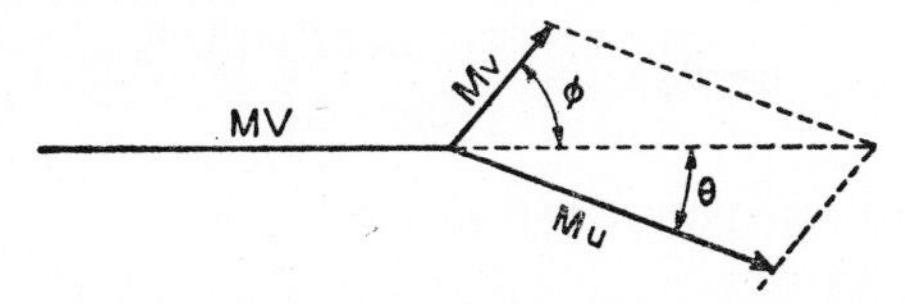

Fig. 3.—Conservation of impulse after impact of particles.

Consider a particle A, of mass M, in uniform rectilinear motion with velocity $\vec{V}$, and direction such that it enters the field of a second particle, B, of mass m, originally at rest. The approach of A will set B into motion, while its own motion will also be affected. When both particles reach a sufficiently great distance apart, so that their mutual action is no longer appreciable, we shall assume that they are still in motion. Let A now have a velocity $\vec{v}$, smaller than the original $\vec{V}$, and let its path now make an angle ϕ with the original direction, while B will have a velocity $\vec{u}$ at an angle θ to that same direction. (*See* Fig. 3.)

We may call this a collision, and without any assumptions concerning interactions, we know that principles of conservation of energy and momentum have to be satisfied.*

* Under certain circumstances it may happen that some of the kinetic energy of A vanishes as such, and appears as energy of excitation of a complex particle B. Such a collision is said to be inelastic, but in the examples dealt with, elastic collision is always envisaged, no energy loss being involved.

These involve the conditions that $\vec{u}$ and $\vec{v}$ should be on opposite sides of $\vec{V}$, and that all three of these are coplanar, and that the angle $\phi+\theta$ should be less than 180°. Each of these angles may vary between 0° and 180°.

If as axes of reference we take the direction $\vec{V}$, and the perpendicular to this, three equations may be written, expressing the conservation conditions, always assuming that neither of the particles has a velocity great enough for relativistic corrections to become necessary.*

Thus, we have:

$$\left.\begin{aligned} MV &= Mv\cos\phi + mu\cos\phi; \\ 0 &= Mv\sin\phi - mu\sin\phi; \\ MV^2 &= Mv^2 + mu^2. \end{aligned}\right\} \tag{1}$$

These constitute three equations involving four variables, v, u, θ and ϕ, which characterize the system after the collision, and thus we can express any one of these variables in terms of the other three.

Consider θ as fixed. Now in the triangle formed by $\vec{mu}$, $\vec{MV}$ and $\vec{Mv}$, we have

$$\cos\theta = \frac{(MV^2)+(mu)^2-(Mv)^2}{2MVmu}.$$

From the third equation of (1), we have also

$$MV^2-(Mv)^2 = mMu^2$$

and so
$$\cos\theta = \frac{1}{2}\frac{u}{v}\left(1+\frac{m}{M}\right).$$

Hence $\cos\theta$ can never be negative, so that θ can never exceed $\pi/2$. From this we may also deduce that the particle struck must always be projected forwards. Also a projection at an angle of $\pi/2$ must mean $u=0$, so that the velocity will be zero. When θ is 0, the collision is said to be frontal, while when θ is 90°, the collision is tangential.

From equation (1) we may also derive the following:

$$u = V\frac{2M}{M+m}\cos\theta \tag{2}$$

$$v = V\sqrt{\left(1-\frac{4mM}{(M+m)^2}\cos^2\theta\right)} \tag{3}$$

* This problem is dealt with in the relativistic case in *Experimental Nuclear Physics* by E. Segré (Vol. 2, Part VI, Chapter I, by Philip Morrison).

$$\frac{\frac{1}{2}mu^2}{\frac{1}{2}MV^2} = \frac{4mM}{(M+m)^2}\cos^2\theta \tag{4}$$

$$\tan\phi = \frac{m\sin 2\theta}{M-m\cos 2\theta} \tag{5}$$

$$\frac{M+m}{M-m} = \frac{\tan(\theta+\phi)}{\tan\theta} \tag{6}$$

$$\frac{M}{m} = \frac{\sin(\phi+2\theta)}{\sin\phi}. \tag{7}$$

Equations (2) and (3) give the two velocities after collision; equation (4) gives the fraction of kinetic energy lost by A by a transfer to the particle struck; equation (5) enables ϕ to be found; equations (6) and (7) enable us, if θ and ϕ are experimentally found, to determine the ratio of the masses of the particles.

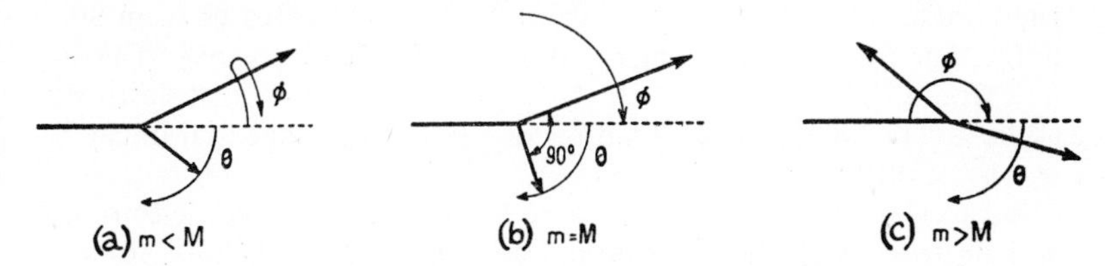

FIG. 4.—Relationship between directions of particles after impact.

Let us now consider three possible mass relationships.

Case I: When $m < M$ (i.e. when the particle struck is lighter than the incident particle) (*see* Fig. 4*a*).

Here $\tan\phi$ will always be positive, and ϕ will be zero when θ is zero, and increasing when θ slowly increases. Thus ϕ passes through a maximum when equation (5) becomes annulled, i.e. when θ assumes a value θ_0, where $\cos 2\theta_0 = m/M$. This corresponds to a value of θ_0 less than 45°, and giving a maximum value for the deviation ϕ the figure

$$\phi_{max} = \arctan\left(\frac{m}{\sqrt{(M^2-m^2)}}\right) = \arcsin\frac{m}{M}.$$

When θ becomes greater than θ_0, ϕ decreases, and becomes zero again when θ is 90°. Thus, for a given value of ϕ, there is a corresponding pair of values of θ, which are obtained by solution of the equation (5) with respect to θ. This gives us

$$\tan\theta = \frac{m\cos\phi \pm \sqrt{(m^2-M^2\sin^2\phi)}}{(M+m)\sin\phi}. \tag{8}$$

If $a = \frac{1}{2}mu^2/\frac{1}{2}MV^2$, then a is the fraction of the kinetic energy imparted by A to B, and this is given by equation (4). This becomes a maximum and equal to $4mM/(m+M)^2$ when B is projected forwards. It decreases as the angle of projection grows, until at an angle of projection equal to 90° annulment occurs. In the special case where m is much smaller than M, the maximum value which u can attain is $2V$. Such is found in the case of the impact between an atomic particle and an electron, the latter being the originally stationary particle.

Case II: When $m=M$ (both particles of the same size or mass) (Fig. 4*b*).

From equation (7) we have

$$\sin(\phi+2\theta) = \sin\phi,$$

and so we have also

$$\phi+\theta = 90°.$$

Thus the angle between the two trajectories after impact is always a right angle, so that as θ grows, from 0 to 90°, ϕ decreases from 90 to 0°. The fraction of the energy transferred is equal to $\cos^2$. Thus, in a frontal impact the particle A becomes motionless, transferring all its kinetic energy to B. Transfer of energy in a tangential impact is, on the other hand, always zero.

Such conditions apply in the case of collisions between electron and electron, neutron and proton, and α-particle and helium atom, etc., provided that the energies do not involve relativistic corrections.

Case III: When $m > M$ (i.e. the particle struck is lighter than the incident particle) (*see* Fig. 4*c*).

Tan ϕ now has a negative sign, θ being smaller than θ_0, and $\cos 2\theta_0$ is thus equal to M/m.

When θ is 0, ϕ will be 180°, so that A will retrace its path after having projected particle B forwards. The fraction of energy which is transferred has a maximum value of $4mM/(M+m)^2$.

As θ increases, ϕ decreases in the same proportion as the energy transferred; ϕ equals 90° when $\theta=\theta_0$ ($\theta < 45°$). When θ tends towards 90°, ϕ continues to decrease, and tends towards zero. The energy transfer is always zero in case of a tangential impact.

There is only one value of θ which leads to any fixed value of ϕ, and the corresponding expression is

$$\tan\theta = \frac{m\cos\phi + \sqrt{(m^2 - M^2\sin^2\phi)}}{(M+m)\sin\phi}. \tag{9}$$

The conditions for this third case are fulfilled in the example of an electron striking a nucleus, or when an α-particle strikes a nucleus heavier than that of helium. Other examples are known.

(2) Introduction of Impact Parameter

The foregoing conclusions are valid whatever the force exerted between two particles, and enable us to describe the characteristics of the motion after impact as functions of one arbitrary parameter, such as the angle θ.

If the law of force is known, calculation of this parameter in terms of the conditions governing the original motion of B enables us to deduce all the other dimensions involved.

The initial kinematic conditions of velocity and direction of motion were introduced above and the only arbitrary condition which remains is the respective positions of the two particles. This may be defined by the distance of the initial rectilinear trajectory of A towards B, i.e. the minimum approach distance between the two particles, assuming no interaction. This distance, symbolized by p, we call the impact parameter. The problem now becomes one of finding the value of θ as a function of the impact parameter in order to calculate the values characterizing conditions after impact.

From the experimental point of view, the impact parameter can neither be selected nor measured before the collision.

On the other hand, if the law of interaction is known, observation of one of the dimensions defining movement after collision enables us to evaluate the impact parameter. Actually, this is hardly an interesting result.

It so happens that in a great number of experimental circumstances, one is dealing not with a single collision but with many, and it is not possible to evaluate the impact parameter in each case, but for the collection of collisions involved one can define the law of probability which determines the distribution of the p-values. To each p-value corresponds a determined value of the dimensions resulting from the impact, and so one can calculate for the collection of collisions the distribution law for each of the dimensions.

Let us consider a typical case. Imagine a particle A arriving at random on a surface S, in which there is a particle B. The probability that the impact parameter will have a value less than p is given by $\pi p^2/S$, since we have only to consider p-values which are very small by comparison with linear dimensions of S. In actual fact, there is never a single B-particle, but a distribution with a density of n particles per sq. cm., or nS on the surface concerned. If we consider only p-values small in comparison with distance between B-particles, the probability that particle A will pass nearer than a distance p to any B-particle is given by $n\pi p^2$, and the probability that it will pass at a distance p from the B-particle is $2n\pi p\,dp$.

(3) The Case of Coulombic Interaction

Let us suppose that the particle A carries a charge Ze, and the particle B a charge of ze, charges which may be of the same sign, or of opposite sign. We shall now endeavour to establish the relation between the impact parameter and the projection angle θ.

We shall make use of a theorem in classical mechanics by which we can study the relative motion of two particles, by taking reference axes with fixed directions, making one of the particles the point of origin, so that the other will have a reduced mass μ, given by

$$\frac{1}{\mu} = \frac{1}{M}+\frac{1}{m} \qquad \text{or} \qquad \mu = \frac{Mm}{M+m}.$$

Thus, if B is taken as origin, the movement of A will be Keplerian (*see* Fig. 5). The trajectory of A will thus be a hyperbola with B as focus. The angle α between the two asymptotes will then represent

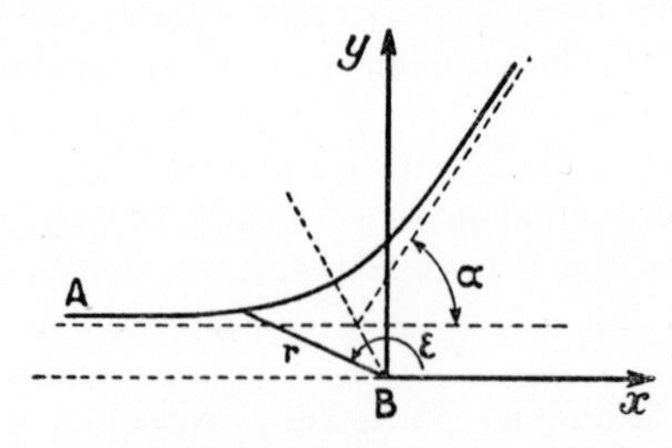

FIG. 5.—Movement of an incident particle in a system of reference relative to the struck particle.

the deviation of particle A. The value of α can be derived if we write the equation of motion by projection upon an axis Bx parallel to the initial velocity. Thus we have

$$\mu\frac{dv_x}{dt} = \frac{Zze^2}{r^2}\cos\epsilon,$$

in which r is the vector radius, and ϵ the polar angle.

By integration of this we get

$$\mu(V\cos\alpha - V) = Z\epsilon e^2 \int_{-\infty}^{+\infty} \frac{\cos\epsilon}{r^2}\,dt.$$

The kinetic moment is constant, and equal to its initial value, so that

$$\mu Vp = -\mu r^2\frac{d\epsilon}{dt},$$

from which is obtained

$$\frac{1}{r^2} = -\frac{1}{pV}\frac{d\epsilon}{dt},$$

and when this combined with the former expression, we arrive at

$$\mu V(\cos\alpha - 1) = -\frac{Zze^2}{pV}\int_{\pi}^{\alpha}\cos\epsilon\, d\epsilon = -\frac{Zze^2}{pV}\sin\alpha.$$

Hence we get
$$\frac{\sin\alpha}{1-\cos\alpha} = \cot\frac{\alpha}{2} = p\frac{\mu V^2}{Zze^2},$$

and if we now put

$$b = \frac{2Zze^2}{\mu V^2} = \frac{Zze^2}{E}\left(1+\frac{M}{m}\right), \tag{10}$$

we get
$$\cot\frac{\alpha}{2} = \frac{2p}{b}. \tag{11}$$

The value b is the distance at which the potential energy Zze^2/b is equal to the kinetic energy $\frac{1}{2}\mu V^2$ of the incident particle. In two particles of the same sign, this is also the minimum distance of approach, only possible in frontal collision.

Equation (11) gives us thus the relation between the impact parameter and the deviation in the co-ordinate system which we have considered.

The components of the velocity of B along the two fixed axes are

$$u\cos\theta \quad \text{and} \quad -u\sin\theta,$$

while the components of the velocity of A are

$V\cos\alpha$ and $V\sin\alpha$ with respect to the system B

and $v\cos\phi$ and $v\sin\phi$ with respect to the fixed system.

Hence, it may be deduced that

$$v\cos\phi = V\cos\alpha + u\cos\theta$$

and

$$v\sin\phi = V\sin\alpha - u\sin\theta,$$

from which it follows that

$$\tan\alpha = \frac{v\sin\phi + u\sin\theta}{v\cos\phi - u\cos\theta}.$$

From this last expression, taken in conjunction with equation (1),

$$\tan\alpha = \tan 2\theta,$$

so that
$$\theta = \frac{\pi}{2} - \frac{\alpha}{2}. \tag{12}$$

This, together with equation (11), leads to the relation between impact parameter and the angle of projection θ, i.e.

$$\tan\theta = \frac{2p}{b} \tag{13}$$

and as, from equation (5),

$$\tan\phi = \frac{m\sin 2\theta}{M-m\cos 2\theta} = \frac{2m\tan\theta}{(M-m)+(M+m)\tan^2\theta}.$$

The relation between p and ϕ is given by

$$\tan\phi = \frac{4}{\dfrac{b}{p}\left(\dfrac{M}{m}-1\right)+\dfrac{4p}{b}\left(\dfrac{M}{m}+1\right)}. \tag{14}$$

If the probability of a particle passing at a distance between p and $p+\mathrm{d}p$ is

$$\mathrm{d}\varpi_p = 2\pi np\,\mathrm{d}p,$$

the probability of this particle having a deviation between ϕ and $\phi+\mathrm{d}\phi$ is

$$\mathrm{d}\varpi_\phi = 2\pi np(\phi)\frac{\mathrm{d}p}{\mathrm{d}\phi}.\mathrm{d}\phi.$$

If equation (14) is solved, with respect to p, and making use of the expression for p in terms of ϕ, this last expression gives

$$\mathrm{d}\varpi_\phi = \frac{2Z^2z^2e^4}{M^2V^4}\pi n\frac{\left[\cos\phi\pm\sqrt{\left(1-\dfrac{M^2}{m^2}\sin^2\phi\right)}\right]^2}{\sin^3\phi\sqrt{\left(1-\dfrac{M^2}{m^2}\sin^2\phi\right)}}\mathrm{d}\phi.$$

Finally the probability of deviation through a solid angle Ω in the direction ϕ is given by

$$\mathrm{d}\varpi_\Omega = \frac{Z^2z^2e^4n}{M^2V^4}\frac{\left[\cos\phi\pm\sqrt{\left(1-\dfrac{M^2}{m^2}\sin^2\phi\right)}\right]^2}{\sin^4\phi\sqrt{\left(1-\dfrac{M^2}{m^2}\sin^2\phi\right)}}.$$

This is known as the Rutherford formula, and if one calls $\mathrm{d}\sigma_\Omega(\phi)$ the differential effective section for deviation within the angle $\mathrm{d}\Omega$ making an angle ϕ with the initial direction, one has also

$$\mathrm{d}\sigma_\Omega = \frac{Z^2z^2e^4}{M^2V^4}\frac{\left[\cos\phi\pm\sqrt{\left(1-\dfrac{M^2}{m^2}\sin^2\phi\right)}\right]^2}{\sin^4\phi\sqrt{\left(1-\dfrac{M^2}{m^2}\sin^2\phi\right)}}\mathrm{d}\Omega. \tag{15}$$

In this expression, if $m > M$, then the positive sign is used; in the contrary case, the two signs correspond to two possible values of θ associated with ϕ, so that if one is interested only in ϕ, the probability is the sum of the two probabilities in question.

Consider now the fraction of kinetic energy transferred by A to B. According to equation (4) this is given by

$$a = \frac{4mM}{(M+m)^2}\cos^2\theta = k\cos^2\theta \tag{16}$$

and can vary between zero and $4mM/(M+m)^2$, this expression being always less than unity except when $m = M$.

What is the probability of an energy transfer between the limits a and $a+\mathrm{d}a$? This will be

$$\mathrm{d}a = 2\pi np(a)\frac{\mathrm{d}p}{\mathrm{d}a}.\mathrm{d}a = \pi n\frac{\mathrm{d}(p^2)}{\mathrm{d}a}.\mathrm{d}a$$

or
$$p^2(a) = \frac{b^2}{4}\tan^2\theta = \frac{b^2}{4}\frac{(k-a)}{a},$$

so that
$$\frac{\mathrm{d}p^2}{\mathrm{d}a} = -\frac{b^2k}{4a^2}$$

whence
$$\mathrm{d}\varpi_a = \pi n\frac{b^2}{4}\frac{k}{a^2}\mathrm{d}a = \frac{\pi nZ^2z^2e^4}{E^2}\cdot\frac{M}{m}\cdot\frac{\mathrm{d}a}{a^2}.$$

It should be noted that the minus sign before the expression $\mathrm{d}p/\mathrm{d}a$ need not be retained. In fact, when we write $\mathrm{d}p/\mathrm{d}a$ we express merely the increment of the variable p corresponding to the increment $\mathrm{d}a$ of the variable a. Thus, we are not concerned with the absolute value of this increment nor with the minus sign, which merely indicates that p and a vary in opposite sense, so that the minus sign can be neglected. This, in future, will be done generally in the calculations.

If the energy lost, i.e. aE, is denoted by ϵ, one can say that the probability of an energy loss between the limits ϵ and $\epsilon+\mathrm{d}\epsilon$ will be

$$\mathrm{d}\varpi_\epsilon = \frac{\pi nZ^2z^2e^4}{E}\frac{M}{m}\frac{\mathrm{d}\epsilon}{\epsilon^2}, \tag{17}$$

which indicates that the probability is higher in the case of small energy losses, at least between the limits 0 and KE (Fig. 6).

The sum of the probabilities $\int_0^{KE}\mathrm{d}\varpi_\epsilon$ is infinite, which is physically meaningless. This is because integration from zero value can have no physical reality.

It would relate, in fact, to infinite impact parameter, which cannot be realized. Such a formula presupposes that the deviation is due to the intervention of a single diffusing centre, i.e. we assume that the impact parameter relative to one of the particles in the layer which is traversed is much smaller than with respect to others. This is true only if we assume impact parameters which are small compared with the mean distance of projection of the particle B on a plane perpendicular to the trajectory of A. This is why, just as in the case of the Rutherford formula, the energy transfer formula ceases to be valid in the case of tangential impacts (which involve large impact parameters, small deviations and minute energy transfers), the limit being dependent upon the number of diffusing centres per unit area of the layer traversed.

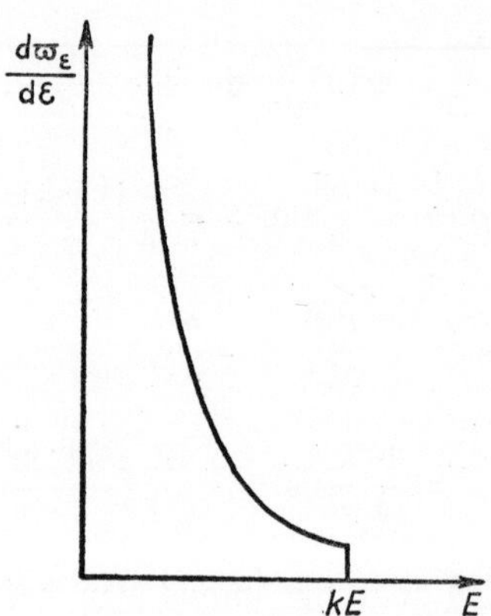

FIG. 6.—Probability of energy transfer during a coulombic impact.

(4) INTERACTION WITH A DEFINITE RADIUS OF ACTION

We shall now consider another law of force. We shall suppose that interaction of two corpuscles is zero when their distance apart is greater than a certain value R and that for distances less than R there is a repulsive force, the magnitude of which is a function of the distance. We shall call R the radius of action.

For corpuscles governed by such a law of interaction there is a collision only when the impact parameter is less than R, so that calculations may be broken down into two sections. The probability required is the product of two probabilities—that for an impact represented by the relative value πR^2, called the effective cross-section for impact, and that given for the given value being applicable once impact has occurred. In coulombic interaction in $1/r^2$, such separation is impossible, as the force varies relatively slowly as a function of distance so that one cannot delineate any definite radius of action.

Let us therefore imagine that impact has already occurred, and that we are concerned, then, with the second factor.

We make use of the same symbols as before and start by investigating what happens in a system referred to B.

Let p be the impact parameter ($p < R$); then the trajectory of A is rectilinear to the point M at a distance R from B, from which strong repulsive forces now emanate (Fig. 7).

Such forces depend only on the distance and act along the vector radius. Thus the trajectory remains in the plane fixed by the initial trajectory and the particle B, and $r^2(\mathrm{d}\epsilon/\mathrm{d}t)$ is constant. This means that $\mathrm{d}\epsilon/\mathrm{d}t$ has the same value for two points having the same radius vector, and the trajectory offers an axis of symmetry By.

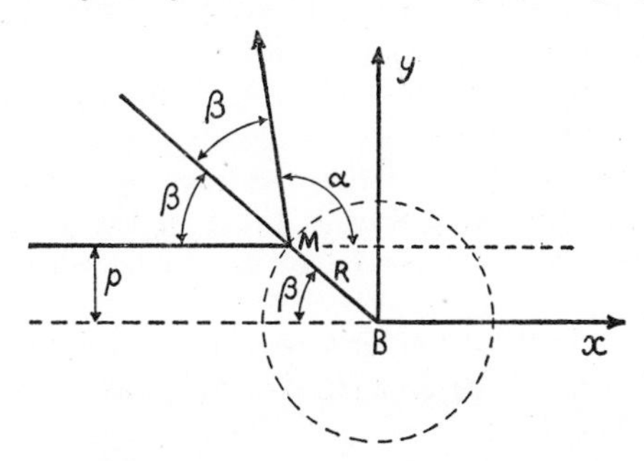

FIG. 7.—Movement of an incident particle in a system of reference relative to the particle struck (repulsive force with definite radius of action).

If the repulsive forces are great enough to prevent penetration of A into the sphere of radius R, the symmetry axis is virtually BM. We may consider then that A is reflected from the surface of a sphere at an angle equal to the angle of incidence. Thus, the deviation (α) of A is

$$\alpha = \pi - 2\beta,$$

while

$$\sin\beta = \frac{p}{R}. \tag{18}$$

The probability of an impact parameter between p and $p+\mathrm{d}p$ is $2p\,\mathrm{d}p/R^2$, and that of a deviation between α and $\alpha+\mathrm{d}\alpha$ is

$$\mathrm{d}\varpi_\alpha = \frac{2}{R^2}p(\alpha)\frac{\mathrm{d}p}{\mathrm{d}\alpha}.\mathrm{d}\alpha.$$

Thus we have also

$$p(\alpha) = R\sin\left(\frac{\pi}{2}-\frac{\alpha}{2}\right) = R\cos\frac{\alpha}{2}$$

and

$$\frac{\mathrm{d}p}{\mathrm{d}\alpha} = -\frac{R}{2}\sin\frac{\alpha}{2}.$$

Once more dropping the minus sign, which signifies that p and α are in opposite sense, we have

$$d\varpi = \tfrac{1}{2}\sin\alpha\,.\,d\alpha.$$

$\frac{1}{2}\sin\alpha\,.\,d\alpha$ represents the fraction of the total solid angle 4π between the directions α and $\alpha+d\alpha$, and the result signifies that diffusion within the fixed element of solid angle is proportional only to this solid angle, and independent of the direction. In other words, the diffusion is isotropic. Such a result is valid only in a system of co-ordinates in fixed directions relative to the diffusing particle or to the centre of gravity, the diffusion angle being the same for both systems. If one considers a position of A after the impact, and sufficiently far from A that one can neglect the impact parameter with regard to BA, and thus take BA as the trajectory of A in a system relating to B, the centre of gravity G of the two particles is displaced towards BA. If the axes relating to G are parallel to the fixed axes in the same way as those of the system relating to B, then A describes in this system also a trajectory GB with an inclination α.

The deflection in the observer's system can easily be studied. The probability that it will be between ϕ and $\phi+d\phi$ is given by

$$d\varpi_\phi = \frac{2}{R^2}p(\phi)\frac{dp}{d\phi}d\phi = \frac{1}{R^2}\frac{d(p^2)}{d\phi}d\phi.$$

Now, if the angle of projection of B is θ, one obtains from equation (12)

$$\theta = \frac{\pi}{2}-\frac{\alpha}{2} = \beta,$$

θ and ϕ being related via equations (8) or (9).

Consequently, from equation (18) we get

$$p = R\sin\theta$$

and

$$d\varpi_\phi = d\phi\frac{d(\sin^2\theta)}{d\phi} = \frac{2\tan\theta}{(1+\tan^2\theta)^2}\frac{d(\tan\theta)}{d\phi}d\phi. \qquad (19)$$

The expression (8) for $\tan\theta$ as a function of ϕ allows us now to express $d\varpi_\phi$ as a function of ϕ and leads to a somewhat complicated expression which will not be given here for the general case. For the special case, however, when $m=M$, we know that $\theta=(\pi/2)-\phi$, and hence

$$d\varpi_\Phi = d\phi\frac{d(\cos^2\phi)}{d\phi} = 2\sin\phi\cos\phi\,d\phi. \qquad (20)$$

The probability of a deflection within the solid angle $\mathrm{d}\Omega$ around a direction making an angle ϕ with the original direction is

$$\mathrm{d}\varpi_\phi = \frac{\cos\phi}{\pi}\,\mathrm{d}\Omega. \tag{21}$$

Now consider probability of energy loss. The probability of transfer to B of a fraction of the energy lying between a and $a+\mathrm{d}a$ is given by

$$\mathrm{d}\varpi_a = \frac{2}{R^2}p(a)\frac{\mathrm{d}p}{\mathrm{d}a}\mathrm{d}a = \frac{1}{R^2}\frac{\mathrm{d}(p^2)}{\mathrm{d}a}.\mathrm{d}a,$$

so that we have also

$$a = k\cos^2\theta \qquad \text{and} \qquad k = \frac{4mM}{(M+m)^2}$$

and also $$p = R\sin\theta,$$

and hence we obtain $$p^2 = R^2\left(1-\frac{a}{k}\right)$$

and thus $$\mathrm{d}\varpi_a = \frac{\mathrm{d}a(M+m)^2}{4mM}. \tag{22}$$

We have seen that a can vary between zero and $4mM/(M+m)^2$, and equation (22) shows that all energy losses within this interval are equally probable.

In the case of equal masses, equation (22) becomes

$$\mathrm{d}\varpi_a = \mathrm{d}a. \tag{23}$$

Thus, all energy losses between zero and the initial energy are equally probable.

The equations derived in this paragraph are used in problems of the deceleration of neutrons of less than 10 Mev by impact on atomic nuclei, and when these nuclei are protons, the simplified forms (21) and (23) become applicable.

Chapter 3

GENERALITIES ON ATOMS IN MOTION

The first radiations which we shall study are those of moving atoms, whose behaviour during their passage through matter we shall investigate. It is important first of all to fix on some points of terminology in order to avoid confusion. An ordinary atom possesses a nucleus surrounded by a number of electrons, although an atom moving in a material medium will lose some of its electrons, and its nucleus will retain a number of electrons around it, this number decreasing as the velocity of the atom increases. Thus an α-particle is a helium atom reduced to its nucleus, the electrons being removed at an energy of 1 Mev, but during deceleration the acquisition of one electron followed by another gives back the helium atom. A fission fragment emitted with a kinetic energy of 80 Mev will have lost perhaps twenty electrons, which will be regained at the expense of the medium proportionately with the degree of deceleration.

For whatever atom we choose to consider there will be a certain speed at which, if the atom travels through matter, it becomes deprived of its electrons and reduced to its nucleus. Below this velocity the nucleus gradually re-acquires electrons, and at very low speeds the complete, electrically-neutral atom is re-formed. Only the highest of elements can be so energized that they become deprived of all their electrons.

Thus the study of a moving atom becomes virtually that of ionized atoms, this ionization being more complete the greater the velocity, and in the case of light atoms complete ionization may easily be achieved, as with hydrogen and helium. Of these elements the nuclei are usually referred to as the proton and the α-particle.

Sometimes used as alternatives, then, are the terms: atom, ionized atom, ion, nucleus. From our point of view it may be preferable then to make use of the less precise term 'atomic particle'.

(1) Circumstances Producing Atom Movement

The atom of smallest atomic number ($Z=1$) is hydrogen. There are in this case three isotopes—ordinary hydrogen, heavy hydrogen or deuterium, and tritium, the mass numbers of these being respectively 1, 2 and 3. The corresponding nuclei are known as proton, deuteron, and triton.

It is common practice to accelerate the first two of these nuclei in the various types of accelerating machines at present available. The range of kinetic energies within which it is possible to do this is from very low values up to above 6 Gev (as in the Berkeley synchrotron), though recent developments seem likely to push this upper limit as high as several tens of Gev. Protons with this order of energy or even higher are observed in cosmic rays. Tritons have been accelerated also, but are rare and costly, and so not frequently employed.

The nuclei of the hydrogen isotopes can be expelled from various more complex nuclei by a number of nuclear reactions, of which they form the secondary products.

The element of atomic number 2 is helium, of which only the isotopes of mass 3 and 4 are of interest.

Ordinary helium is isotope 4, the nucleus being particularly stable, and composed of two neutrons and two protons joined together with a binding energy of 28 Mev. This nucleus is the helion or α-particle, which is emitted spontaneously by certain nuclei (usually of mass greater than 200), in the course of radioactivity. For many years, before accelerators were developed, radioactivity α-particles were the only light atomic moving particles available to experimenters, so that they played an historic rôle and have been the subject of much investigation. Nowadays accelerators enable us to obtain much more intense sources of α-particles than are possible with natural radioactive materials alone.

The latter, although yielding α-particles of very definite energies, are not so convenient to use except for certain particular energy values between 5 and 8 Mev, while the particle from accelerators may be obtained with energy ranges between zero and above 400 Mev (as in the frequency-modulated cyclotron at Berkeley).

Many nuclear reactions result in the emission of secondary α-particles, and in a similar way helium 3 may be produced in motion. While in principle this isotope, being stable, might be separated and isolated, in actual fact it is such a rare isotope that little work has been done on it in accelerators.

Atoms of atomic number greater than 2 have only quite recently been observed in motion as a result of nuclear reactions, or as the result of collision induced by other moving particles. Heavy atoms very rarely receive sufficient energy to set them in motion. A notable exception, however, is provided by the products of nuclear fission or the splitting of a heavy nucleus into two parts. Such fission gives rise to nuclei of elements in the middle part of the periodic classification with energies of several tens of Mev.

Another exception is provided by the recoil atoms in α radioactivity; these are heavy atoms which although having received kinetic energies of only about a hundred kev have nevertheless been observed in their short paths.

Various workers have recently succeeded in accelerating in cyclotrons certain ions heavier than α-particles, e.g. C, N, O, but little has been published in this respect.

Experiments have been carried out on moving particles which fall under the headings of (*a*) light nuclei, such as the proton and the α-particle, and (*b*) nuclei of medium mass, such as those emitted during nuclear fission. Both of these groups may now be discussed further.

Chapter 4

VARIATION OF CHARGE ON LIGHT ATOMS IN MOTION

(1) VARIATION IN CHARGE ON THE PROTON

Let us consider an ionized hydrogen atom, i.e. a proton, travelling with a velocity V, and let p_1 be the probability per unit length of trajectory that this proton will take up an electron and so become converted into a hydrogen atom. In a trajectory increment dx, such probability will amount to $p_1 \mathrm{d}x$. We may now express p_1 in the form $p_1 = N\sigma_1$, where N is the number of atoms per c.c. in the medium traversed, while σ_1 will be the effective cross-section of these atoms for electron capture. Quite obviously p_1, and σ_1 will be functions of V.

Now, if a proton penetrates into a material medium, the probability that at the end of a journey of length x it has not captured an electron is given by $\mathrm{e}^{-p_1 x}$ or $\mathrm{e}^{-N\sigma_1 x}$. We may put $N\sigma_1 = 1/\lambda_1$ so that the preceding probability becomes $\mathrm{e}^{-x/\lambda_1}$, the distribution law for probability of path before capture is exponential and corresponds to the mean free path λ_1.

In the same way, considering a neutral hydrogen atom the probability per unit length of path that an electron will be lost will be p_0, related to the effective atomic cross-section σ_0 and a mean free path λ_0 in the neutral state by the expressions

$$p_0 = N\sigma_0 \qquad \lambda_0 = \frac{1}{N\sigma_0}.$$

Now imagine a bundle of particles penetrating matter and composed of $n_0(0)$ neutral atoms of hydrogen and $n_1(0)$ ionized atoms. After passing through a distance x in the medium, the bundle now consists of $n_0(x)$ neutral hydrogen atoms and $n_1(x)$ ionized atoms. Then we have the differential equations

$$\mathrm{d}n_0 = -\, n_0 p_0 \mathrm{d}x + n_1 p_1 \mathrm{d}x$$

$$\mathrm{d}n_1 = +\, n_0 p_p \mathrm{d}x - n_1 p_1 \mathrm{d}x.$$

Suppose the change in velocity in the path x is very small, so that p_0 and p_1 can be taken as constant, then integration of these equations gives us:

$$n_0(x) = [n_1(0)+n_0(0)]\frac{p_1}{p_1+p_0} + \left[n_0(0) - [n_1(0)+n_0(0)]\frac{p_1}{p_1+p_0}\right]\mathrm{e}^{-(p_1+p_0)x}$$

and

$$n_1(x) = [n_1(0)+n_0(0)]\frac{p_0}{p_1+p_0} + \left[n_1(0)-[n_1(0)+n_0(0)]\frac{p_0}{p_1+p_0}\right]e^{-(p_1+p_0)x}$$

These expressions show that the composition of the bundle tends asymptotically to the limiting value $\frac{n_0(x)}{n_1(x)} = \frac{p_1}{p_0} = \frac{\sigma_1}{\sigma_0}$ and compensating variations in charge are constantly occurring.

When this equilibrium charge is attained, there will still be for each individual particle continual variations in charge corresponding to free paths λ_0 and λ_1, but the equilibrium indicates that in any given path element there will be compensating numbers of charges in opposite senses so that the ratio $n_0(x)/n_1(x)$ remains statistically constant.

The variation between composition at entry and the limiting composition decreases with depth of penetration, according to the exponential $e^{-(p_1+p_0)x}$ corresponding to a mean free path $\lambda = 1/(p_1+p_0)$ which can be determined from the expression $\frac{1}{\lambda} = \frac{1}{\lambda_1}+\frac{1}{\lambda_0}$ and which is obviously less than the smaller of these two separate paths λ_1 and λ_0.

Thus, at the end of several free paths of length λ, the relative intensity of the charged component and of the neutral component of the bundle of particles will give the ratio of the cross-section σ_1 and σ_0.

(2) Hall's Experiments[1]

A monokinetic bundle of protons from an acceleration is made to impinge upon a thin metal foil so that the beam, initially composed of charged particles, reaches an equilibrium during its passage through the medium and is analysed upon emergence into the charged component and the neutral component.

The set-up of the apparatus is shown in Fig. 8.

The proton beam, having been energy-selected by magnetic means after leaving the accelerator, travels within the evacuated enclosure formed by the tube joining the accelerator T to the chamber C. The beam is defined by the diaphragm D before striking the thin foil F. Then the beam passes between the pair of electrodes E_1E_2 before reaching the sodium iodide crystal in which scintillations are produced. The luminous intensity corresponding to the beam intensity is measured by the photomultiplier P. Without any potential across E_1E_2 the entire beam strikes the crystal A and the total intensity is measured. When a potential is applied across E_1E_2, the charged component of the beam is deflected and only the neutral component is measured. By difference, the charged component is found.

It is obviously necessary that the thickness of the foil should equal several λ in order to ensure charge equilibrium, but such a thickness must not cause an appreciable deceleration of the protons, i.e. we must ensure that σ_0 and σ_1, remain constant. This is in fact the case

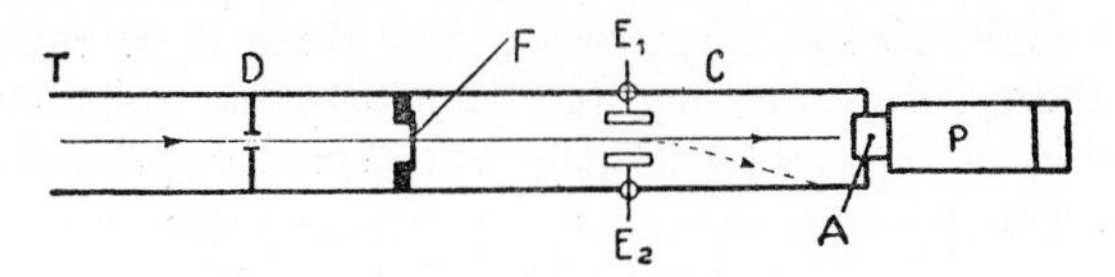

FIG. 8.—Apparatus used by Hall.

when the composition of the emergent beam is unchanged when the foil thickness is varied within such limits that the energy is not appreciably decreased.

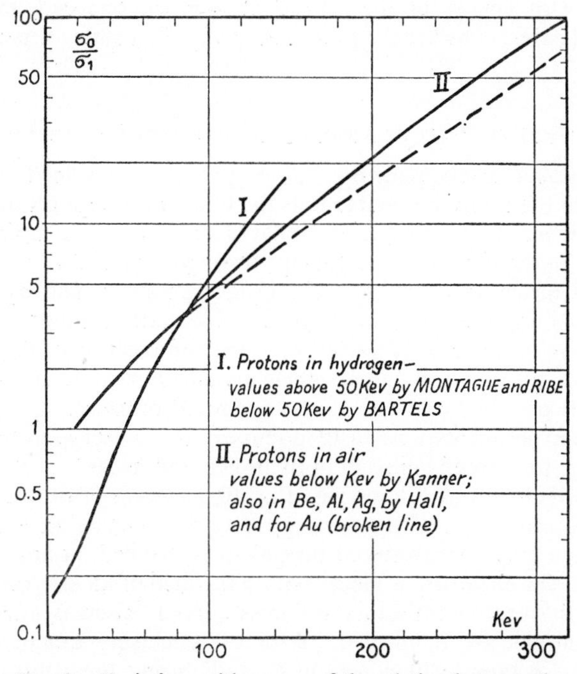

FIG. 9.—Variations with energy of the relation between the effective cross-sections for capture and loss of electrons by protons.

Measurements have been made with foils of beryllium, aluminium, silver and gold, and with protons of energy between 20 and 400 kev. The results are shown in Fig. 9. The estimated accuracy is ± 3 per cent, and the ratio $\sigma_0/\sigma_1 = \lambda_1/\lambda_0$ is the same for the first three elements within the energy range studied but is a little less in the case of gold at energies of 75 kev upwards.

In a first approximation we can say that the ratio between cross-sections is independent of the medium and depends only on the velocity of the proton. It equals 1, 10, and 100 for protons of energies 22·5, 155 and 320 kev respectively. For these three energies the effective charge of the moving ion, defined by the weighting of the two possible charges proportionally with their free paths according to the expression

$$e_{\text{eff}} = \frac{\lambda_1 e}{\lambda_1 + \lambda_0} = e\frac{1}{1+(\sigma_1/\sigma_0)}$$

is respectively $0{\cdot}5e$, $0{\cdot}91e$ and $0{\cdot}99e$.

Above 320 kev the effective charge differs by less than 1 per cent from the limiting charge, and taking into account the very rapid growth with energy of the ratio $\lambda_1/\lambda_0 = \sigma_0/\sigma_1$, one can, in most practical cases, consider the proton as always in a state of maximum charge.

(3) Experiments of Montague, Ribe and Kanner[2, 3, 4]

In the measurements made by Hall, only σ_0/σ_1, is obtained, because even with the thinnest possible foils the thickness is still greater than several mean free paths λ and charge equilibrium is necessarily attained in the course of the passage through such foils.

Direct measurement of effective cross-sections σ_0 and σ_1 or the corresponding free paths should be possible under conditions which enable one to observe the variation in the composition of the beam, i.e. during passage through a sufficiently small amount of material, such as is possible only with gases at reduced pressure.

In the experiments now to be discussed, the object is to measure σ_0 and σ_1 for protons moving in hydrogen and in air.

The principle is as follows (*see* Fig. 10): a beam of protons from an accelerator fitted with an energy selector traverses an enclosure into which may be introduced the gas to be studied, at any desired pressure. The enclosure is placed within the field of an electromagnet so that the proton trajectory becomes curved, whereas uncharged neutral atoms are unaffected. With the enclosure evacuated the bundle of protons will penetrate it, and during the course of its passage through the thin foil F, attains the composition corresponding to a charge equilibrium depending upon the energy used. The magnetic field separates the charged and uncharged components. The uncharged component strikes the detector D_0 situated on the beam axis, while the charged component, by suitable choice of the magnetic field, strikes the detector D_1. For measurement of the effective cross-section σ_0 for ionization hydrogen atoms, the detector

D should be of the 'electron multiplier' type, giving a response proportional to the number of particles striking it, without discrimination between charged and uncharged particles. The reading of D_0 is measured as a function of the gas pressure, readings being taken at several pressure values. If I_0 is the reading *in vacuo*, then that at a pressure P will be given by $I_0 e^{-l/\lambda_0} = I_0 e^{-lN\sigma_0}$, because at the moment of ionization of the neutral atom the magnetic field causes it to leave the beam (trajectories A, B). In this formula l represents the distance between the window F and the detector, while N is the number of gas atoms per c.c. (calculated from the pressure). The measure of the intensity at various pressure values indicates an exponential decrease, and gives the value of σ_0.

In order to measure the effective cross-section σ_1 for neutralization of the proton, one adjusts the magnetic field so that, *in vacuo*, the

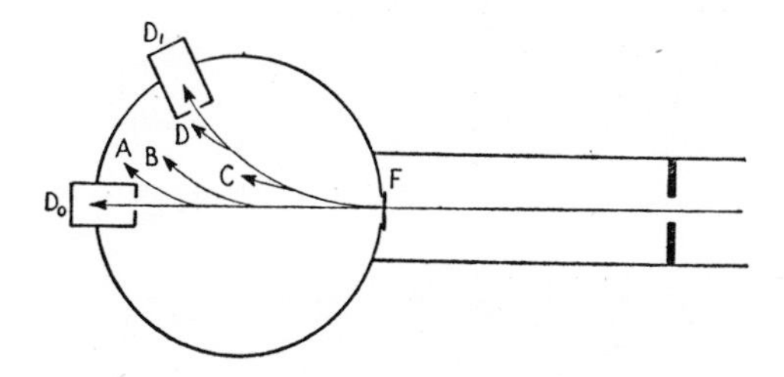

FIG. 10.—Set-up for measurement of absolute values of the effective cross-sections for capture and loss of electrons by protons.

charged component issues from the window F and enters the detector D_1 which is a Faraday's cage sensitive to single charged particles. When a gas at low pressure is introduced into the enclosure, each proton which captures an electron ceases to come under the action of the field and travels off at a tangent at the point of capture (trajectories C, D). Thus the intensity measured by D_1 decreased according to the exponential law

$$I_1 e^{-l_1/\lambda_1} = I_1 e^{-l_1 N\sigma_1}$$

so that σ_1 can be determined.

It will be noted that the magnitude of the cross-section in question (of the order of 10^{-17} sq. cm.) necessitates working at pressures in the region of some hundredths of a millimetre of mercury in order that the free paths λ_0 and λ_1 should be of the same order of magnitude as the dimensions of the apparatus (some 10 cm.). The authors already mentioned have worked with hydrogen and with air, and some results are collected together in Figs. 9 and 11. These show that both σ_0 and σ_1 are decreasing functions of energy, so that both free paths λ_0 and λ_1 increase with increasing energy. However, σ_1 decreases more rapidly than σ_0, the ratio σ_0/σ_1 increasing with energy, signifying that the effective charge increases with energy.

The values of the σ_0/σ_1 values deduced from measurements of σ_0 and σ_1 in air are practically the same as those obtained by Hall for

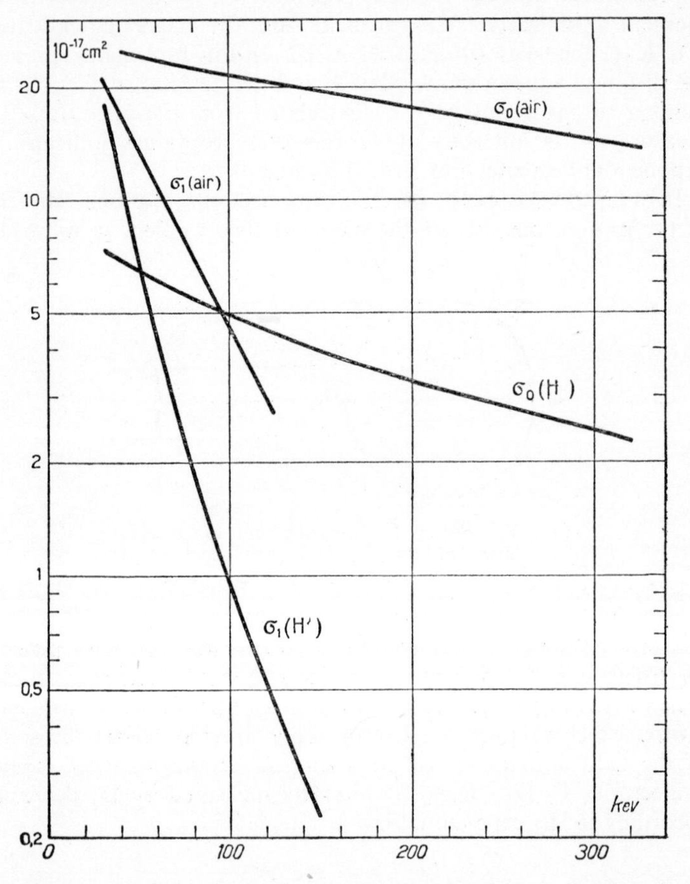

FIG. 11.—Variation in effective cross-section σ_0 and σ_1 as a function of energy in air and hydrogen.

beryllium, aluminium and silver, at least in the energy range common to the two series of determinations (i.e. between 30 and 120 kev). This seems to show that the σ_0/σ_1 ratio depends only on the proton energy and not on the nature of the medium traversed, if one discounts media of atomic number either very low (e.g. hydrogen) or very high (e.g. gold).

As far as orders of magnitude of the effective cross-sections are concerned, these are about 10^{-16} sq. cm., i.e. of the same order as the geometrical cross-sections of the atoms encountered by the moving particles. To these relatively large cross-sections correspond very small mean free paths. A gas under normal conditions of temperature and pressure contains $N = 2{\cdot}69 \times 10^{19}$ molecules per c.c., and the mean free path corresponding to an effective cross-section is in the case of a diatomic gas

$$\frac{1}{2 \times 2{\cdot}69 \times 10^{19} \times 10^{-16}} = 1{\cdot}85 \times 10^{-4} \text{ cm.} = 1{\cdot}8\mu.$$

Thus, a proton of about 100 kev energy changes its charge several hundreds of times in each millimetre of path in a gas under normal conditions.

(4) Variation in Charge of α-Particles

The behaviour of protons is very simple, because the hydrogen atom has but a single electron, so that only two states of charge are possible.

The higher the charge on a nucleus, the greater becomes the complexity of behaviour. In the case of α-particles, three different states of charge are possible: the doubly-charged α-particle, designed He^{++}; the singly-charged ion, He^{+}; and the neutral helium atom, He^{0}.

Measurements of the charges on α-particles were carried out long before similar experiments on protons. They were carried out by Rutherford and his collaborators, notably Henderson[5], around 1924–5, with the aid of natural α-particles from radioactive elements.

To each of the charge states He^{++} and He^{0} there is a corresponding effective cross-section, and these are σ_2 (for electron capture) and σ_0 (for electron loss); the corresponding paths will be λ_2 and λ_0.

In the case of the ion He^{+} there are two cross-sections σ_{12} and σ_{10} for loss and capture of one electron respectively. The corresponding free paths are $\lambda_{12} = 1/N\sigma_{12}$ and $\lambda_{10} = 1/N\sigma_{10}$, and the total free path in the He^{+} state is

$$\lambda_1 = \frac{1}{N(\sigma_{10}+\sigma_{12})} = \frac{\lambda_{10}\lambda_{12}}{\lambda_{10}+\lambda_{12}}.$$

The principle of the measurements carried out on α-particles is the same as that of the experiments described above in connection with protons. The techniques used at the time for the detection of beams (photographic emulsions and scintillations) were less elaborate than present-day methods, and allowed studies to be made at low energies only, and of the exchange $He^{0} \rightleftarrows He^{+}$. For the conditions under which only the exchange $He^{+} \rightleftarrows He^{++}$ becomes appreciable, σ_{10} is negligible compared with σ_{12}, and $\lambda_1 = 1/N\sigma_{12} = \lambda_{12}$.

Experiments have shown that the ratio λ_2/λ_1, equal to the ratio of the intensities of the components He^{++} and He^{+} in the beam in charge equilibrium with the medium, is independent of the nature of the medium (aluminium, mica, copper, silver and gold have been studied) and dependent only on the energy of the particles.

Absolute values of the free paths have been measured in air and are shown in the following table together with corresponding effective cross-sections:

E . .	6·74	4·43	1·68	0·650 Mev
λ_2/λ_1 .	200	67	7·5	1
λ_2. .	2·2	0·52	0·037	0·003 mm.
λ_1. .	0·011	0·0078	0·005	0·003 mm.
σ_2. .	$8{\cdot}4\times10^{-20}$	$3{\cdot}6\times10^{-19}$	5×10^{-18}	6×10^{-17}cm^2
σ_1. .	$1{\cdot}7\times10^{-17}$	$2{\cdot}4\times10^{-17}$	$3{\cdot}7\times10^{-17}$	6×10^{-17}cm^2

It will be noticed that the energy of 650 kev, below which the α-particle is more often singly-charged than doubly-charged, is not a low value, and that it is not necessary to slow down by very much the particles emitted by natural radioelements in order that the charge variations should become appreciable. The effective charge $\frac{2\lambda_2+1\lambda_1}{\lambda_2+\lambda_1}e$ at the four energies indicated above is respectively $1{\cdot}995e$, $1{\cdot}985e$, $1{\cdot}88e$, $1{\cdot}5e$. These values, especially the last two, should be slightly decreased, to allow for the free path in the neutral state. Approximate determinations indicate for λ_0 in air a value of 10^{-3} mm. at 1·68 Mev, and this leads to an effective charge of

$$\frac{2\lambda_2+\lambda_1}{\lambda_2+\lambda_1+\lambda_0}e = 1{\cdot}83e.$$

Quite recently new measurements have been made by Snitzer[6] on α-particles from an accelerator, of energy varying from 100 to 480 kev, i.e. much below the level of the region explored by the Rutherford apparatus. Essentially, Snitzer examined the variations, as a function of energy, of the fractions of a beam at equilibrium, formed by ions He^0, He^+ and He^{++} in four gases: hydrogen, helium, air, and argon. Figs. 12 and 13 show these variations. It will be seen that at the energies 148, 145, 98 and 115 kev the beam contains above 50 per cent of neutral atom and 50 per cent of singly-charged ions, but virtually no α-particles.

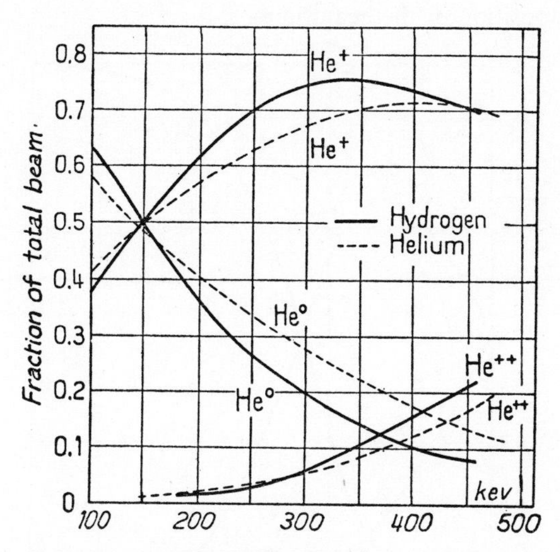

FIG. 12.—Charge equilibrium for α-particles in hydrogen and helium.

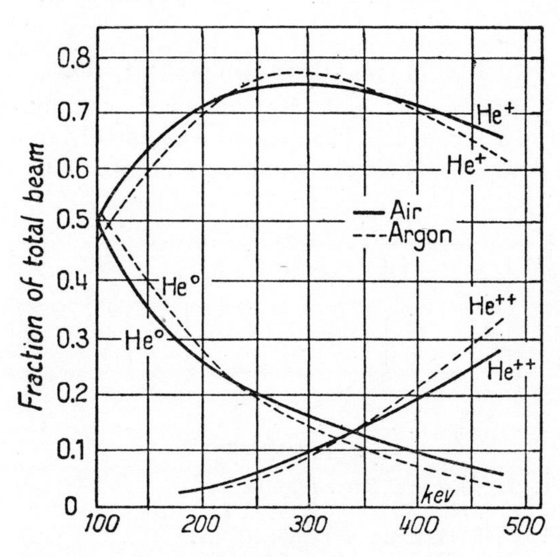

FIG. 13.—Charge equilibrium for α-particles in air and argon.

Fig. 14 shows the results obtained by Snitzer and by Rutherford on the composition of the beam in air.

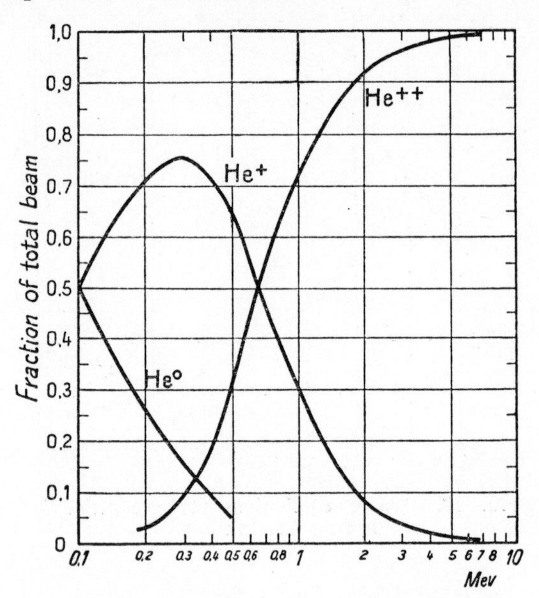

FIG. 14.—Charge equilibrium for α-particles in air.

(5) RESULTS ON OTHER ACCELERATED IONS

Recently, further results have been obtained with nitrogen ions accelerated in a cyclotron. The method is essentially an analysis of the charge composition for an equilibrium beam. Some values are given here:

State of charge .	3+	4+	5+	6+	7+
Ions *N* at 15 Mev [7]	0·4 per cent	6·0 per cent	45·6 per cent	40·5 per cent	7·5 per cent
Ions *N* at 26 Mev [8]		<1 per cent	16 per cent	46 per cent	38 per cent

REFERENCES

1. HALL, T. (1950), *Phys. Rev.*, **79**, 504.
2. MONTAGUE, J. H. (1951), *Phys. Rev.*, **81**, 1026.
3. RIBE, F. L. (1951), *Phys. Rev.*, **83**, 1217.
4. KANNER, H. (1951), *Phys. Rev.*, **84**, 1211.
5. See, for example, RUTHERFORD, CHADWICK and ELLIS, *Radiation from Radioactive Substances*, p. 119.
6. SNITZER, E. (1953), *Phys. Rev.*, **89**, 1237.
7. STEPHENS, K. G., and WALKER, D. (1954), *Phil. Mag.*, **45**, 543.
8. REYNOLDS, H. L., and ZUCKER, A. (1954), *Phys. Rev.*, **95**, 1353.

Chapter 5

DECELERATION OF LIGHT ATOM PARTICLES

(1) General

An atomic particle in motion in a material medium does not retain its kinetic energy, but loses it during a series of interactions with the atoms of the medium traversed. This interaction may be of two kinds, depending on whether it is with electrons or with the nuclei of the atoms of the medium. In the case of the lightest atomic particles, such as the proton and the α-particle, the interactions with nuclei are rare and play a very minor rôle in the deceleration. This rôle, however, becomes increasingly important when we concern ourselves with atomic particles of higher nuclear charge, and when we consider fission fragments the two phenomena are of equal importance. It is necessary, therefore, to consider separately light particles and fission fragments, and the first of these will be dealt with in this chapter.

Let us consider a light atomic particle moving in a material medium. It is an ionized atom carrying with it the electric field which surrounds it. This field acts upon the electrons of atoms in the neighbourhood of the trajectory, and if this action is strong enough, certain electrons become snatched from the atoms to which they were joined, and acquire a certain kinetic energy.

This is ionization, which converts a neutral atom or molecule into two distinct charged bodies, the electron and the positive ion. During this process the kinetic energy of the moving particle is reduced by an amount equal to the sum of the binding energy of the electron released, and the kinetic energy imparted to the latter. Sometimes the reaction may be too weak to cause separation of the electron and ion-pair formation, but may nevertheless change the quantum state of the electron, taking it from an original state of binding energy E_0 to another state where the binding energy is E_1 ($< E_0$). In such a case, we have excitation, and excitation energy $E_0 - E_1$ is imparted to the moving particle as extra kinetic energy.

In the case of light atomic particles, excitation and ionization of atoms or molecules of the medium traversed are practically the only causes of deceleration.

(2) Magnitudes Determining Deceleration

If electrons as components of matter, instead of being attached to atoms, are free, it should be possible to apply to the interaction between moving atomic particles and electrons the general considerations developed in Chapter 2. The mass of the electron is much less than that (M) of any atomic particle; as a result we may say that:

(*a*) the energy imparted to the electron during collision should show a maximum at $4(m/M)$ of that of the incident particle, this proportion being approximately $\frac{1}{500}$ for a proton, and $\frac{1}{2000}$ for an α-particle;

(*b*) the maximum deflection of the electron during collision should be equal to m/M radians (i.e. about 2 and 0·5 minutes of arc for proton and α-particle respectively).

These conclusions remain valid whenever the kinetic energy received by an electron is large compared with its binding energy, so that the latter can be looked upon as negligible. Even if this is not so, and especially in cases of excitation, it remains true that the energy loss of the moving particle remains small compared with the kinetic energy and that the resultant deflection is very small.

From this last feature it follows, at least to a first approximation, that the trajectories of light atomic particles can be looked upon as rectilinear. A more precise treatment will be given later. Consider an atomic particle with kinetic energy T falling normally upon a thin foil of thickness Δx containing n atoms per c.c., these atoms being all of the same kind. In travelling the distance Δx the particle will suffer a certain number of interactions, each involving a very small energy loss (compared with T). Now suppose Δx is large enough to make the number of interactions large compared with unity, although sufficiently small to ensure that the total energy loss ΔT is still small compared with T. The energy left in the particle after traversing the distance Δx is obviously $T-\Delta T$, and it is found that if this quantity is measured for a large number of particles, it varies from particle to particle, although varying only little from the mean value $\overline{\Delta T}$ which one can approximately define as the product of the average number $\bar{k}$ of the interactions suffered by the particle during the course of its passage through the distance Δx and the mean energy $\overline{W}$ lost in one interaction. We must point out that the variations in energy losses are negligible, and that we may well make use of average values. Thus, we can write ΔT in place of $\overline{\Delta T}$.

The energy loss, ΔT, is proportional to Δx, and as a result, the fraction $\Delta T/\mathrm{d}x$ is independent of those values. This ratio depends upon the medium traversed, and upon the type of particle and its kinetic energy.

One can speak of the decelerating power of the medium for the particles of a given type and with given energy. The ratio $\Delta T/\Delta x$ is often expressed in the form $-(\mathrm{d}t/\mathrm{d}x)$, where x is the path length. As T is a function which decreases as x increases, the negative sign is used, as $\Delta T \simeq -\mathrm{d}T$.

This is not rigidly true, since we cannot define a mean energy loss in a strictly physical sense unless Δx is large enough to ensure a large number of interactions. But this limitation is of no practical value, as in reality the circumstances rarely arise where we have to consider paths of such length that few interactions occur.

The decelerating power R is given by

$$R = -\frac{\mathrm{d}T}{\mathrm{d}x}$$

and if we consider the energy loss ΔT within the path Δx we can use

$$\Delta T = R\Delta x$$

provided ΔT remains small compared with T.

In the same way, the decelerating power, instead of being related to length units, can be interpreted in terms of mass units. Thus, we have

$$M = -\frac{\mathrm{d}T}{\mathrm{d}m} = -\frac{\mathrm{d}T}{\mathrm{d}x}\cdot\frac{1}{\mu} = \frac{R}{\mu}$$

where μ is the specific mass of the medium traversed.

Of more interest than R and M is the quantity

$$S = \frac{R}{n} = -\frac{1}{n}\cdot\frac{\mathrm{d}T}{\mathrm{d}x} \quad \text{or} \quad S = \frac{\mu M}{n} = AM$$

where A is the mass of the decelerating atom; S is referred to as the atomic decelerating power, or atomic stopping power. It has the advantage over the other values quoted that it does not depend upon the physical state of the medium considered, but only upon its nature. Thus it is a characteristic for the atomic species constituting the medium.

Some workers have called S the effective atomic stopping section, but this is incorrect, as is clearly seen when we realize that it has the dimensions of energy multiplied by surface area. If we wish to attribute to S the idea of an effective section, we must consider that S is the product of σ, the effective cross-section of interaction of the particle for the atoms of the medium traversed, and the average energy $\overline{W}$ lost per interaction, i.e.

$$S = \sigma.\overline{W}.$$

In actual fact, we are interested only in S, and not in the two separate entities into which it can be resolved.

Further, the fact that the atomic stopping power is constant, and independent of the physical state of the medium traversed, except at very high and possibly also at very low energies, enters into the calculation of energy loss together with the number (n) of atoms per c.c., as in the equation

$$\Delta T = nS\Delta x.$$

It is of interest to see that this allows us to calculate energy loss in a medium composed of various atomic species. If this medium contains in each c.c., n_1, n_2, ..., n_k atoms with stopping powers respectively S_1, S_2, ..., S_k, the energy loss for a trajectory of length Δx is

$$\Delta T = (n_1 S_1 + n_2 S_2 + \ldots + n_k S_k)\Delta x.$$

The stopping is independent, to a fair approximation, of the fact that the atoms of the medium are associated in this or that way in the medium. This property is often called the law of additivity.

It follows, then, that one can calculate the stopping in any medium for which one knows the atomic stopping power of the component elements for the various atomic particles and at various kinetic energies. The stopping power instead of being referred to an atom, is often referred to an electron, and this will be done in future considerations. In such a case it is equal to S/Z. The value of this method of approach is that, at least in the case of energies which are not too small, the quantity S/Z varies little from one atom to another.

It is important to recall that, as we have had occasion to remark in the foregoing paragraphs, the stopping power, in whatever form we choose to consider it, is a function which changes markedly with the energy of the moving particle. In a strict sense, the relation between energy loss and the path traversed is given by

$$x = -\int_{T_0}^{T_0-\Delta T} \frac{dT}{R}$$

and it is only when the interval ΔT is small enough to make R virtually constant that one can write

$$\Delta x = \frac{\Delta T}{R}.$$

(3) The Concept of Equivalent Absorption

One can say that two absorbing layers of different materials are equivalent for a given incident particle of given energy when this particle suffers the same energy loss in passing through the two layers. Let us suppose that the energy losses are so small that one can make use of differential formulæ. Let Δx_1 and Δx_2 be the equivalent thicknesses of two materials containing respectively n_1 and n_2 atoms per c.c., with stopping powers S_1 and S_2. The equivalence of the two layers is then expressed by

$$n_1 S_1 \Delta x_1 = n_2 S_2 \Delta x_2$$

or

$$\frac{\Delta x_2}{\Delta x_1} = \frac{n_1 S_1}{n_2 S_2}.$$

The quantity

$$s_{21} = \frac{S_2}{S_1}$$

is referred to as the relative atomic stopping power of the atoms of the second kind with respect to those of the first kind.

We can also write

$$\Delta x_2 = \frac{n_1}{n_2} \cdot \frac{1}{s_{21}} \cdot \Delta x_1.$$

In practice, the thicknesses traversed are most often measured not in terms of length but in terms of mass. If Δm_1 and Δm_2 are the masses per unit area corresponding to Δx_1 and Δx_2, then

$$\Delta m_1 = n_1 A_1 x_1 \qquad \text{and} \qquad \Delta m_2 = n_2 A_2 \Delta x_2,$$

where A_1 and A_2 are masses of the atoms of types 1 and 2 respectively. Thus,

$$\Delta m_2 = \frac{A_2}{A_1} \cdot \frac{1}{s_{21}} \Delta m_1.$$

The relative atomic stopping power, like the atomic stopping powers from which it is derived, is a function of the energy of the particular incident particle. This variation, however, is generally less marked than that of the individual atomic stopping power and may, for practical purposes, usually be taken as constant between fairly wide limits.

In laboratories in which the properties of moving α-particles have been studied, it has long been customary to take air as the reference material. This is easily understood, because at a time when techniques were but poorly developed, measurements in air were most easily made. At present there is no justification for retaining it as standard, and there is a tendency to adopt for the purpose some chemically well-defined gas, such as argon, or some metal which can be obtained in the form of very thin and very pure foils, such as aluminium.

(4) Theoretical Expression for Stopping Power

The theory of the deceleration of a particle carrying a charge *ze* has been developed by various writers, notably Bethe, Bloch and Möller.

Theory leads to the following expression for the atomic stopping power (Bethe formula):

$$S = \frac{4\pi z^2 e^4}{mv^2} B \quad \text{where} \quad B = Z\left[\log\frac{2mv^2}{I} - \log(1-\beta^2) - \beta^2\right]. \tag{1}$$

In these expressions the significance of the symbols is as follows:

- v: velocity of the moving particle.
- e: electronic charge.
- z, Z: number of unit charges on moving particle and on nuclei of atoms of the medium traversed.
- β: v/c.
- m: mass of electron.
- I: a constant which is characteristic of the atomic species considered and equivalent to the mean energy of ionization of the various electrons in the atom.

If we insert the appropriate numerical values for the constants, the Bethe expression becomes

$$S(\text{Mev.sq.cm.}) = 0{\cdot}510\times 10^{-24} Zz^2 \frac{1}{\beta^2} \times\left[\log\frac{2mc^2}{I} + \log\frac{\beta^2}{1-\beta^2} - \beta^2\right]. \tag{2}$$

The limits of validity of this expression will be dealt with later, and at the moment we need only say it does not hold for very low values of β, and in fact in some cases these would give rise to negative values of S.

The curves shown in Fig. 15 show the variation of S/Z (or stopping power per electron of the decelerating medium) for a proton ($z = 1$) as a function of its kinetic energy. This gives at once the stopping power for particles other than protons, which is proportional to the square of the charge, and since S/Z depends only on β, the scale of the abscissæ is to be multiplied proportionally with the mass.

The nature of the stopping medium is involved in the expression for S/Z only via the constant I. The curves in the figure were for $I = 168$ ev, 301 ev and 790 ev, values which correspond, as we shall see, to aluminium, copper and gold respectively.

The curve shows two portions separated by a minimum which corresponds to a kinetic energy very close to twice the energy equivalent to the rest mass (i.e. about 2 Gev for a proton and 8 Gev for the α-particle). Below this minimum it is the variation of the factor $1/\beta^2$ which preponderates, while above the minimum it is the growth of the logarithmic term.

It should be noted that the stopping power per electron is a little higher for the light atoms than for heavy ones.

In the region of non-relativistic energies, the Bethe formula can be reduced to

$$S(\text{Mev.sq.cm.}) = 0{\cdot}510\times 10^{-24} Zz^2 \frac{1}{\beta^2} \log \frac{2mv^2}{I}. \tag{3}$$

There are two reasons for the limited applicability of this expression:

(*a*) The variation of charge with velocity is small provided the moving atom cannot be considered as reduced to a nucleus. Otherwise, it would be possible to take this effect into account by replacing the z^2 by the mean square of the charge which would be a function of β.

(*b*) The hypothesis on which the little calculation is founded—the formula is justified only when the velocity V of the moving particle is large compared with the orbital velocities of the electrons in the decelerating substances. This is a very important consideration. If, to a first approximation, we equate the binding energy E of an electron with its kinetic energy, this leads to the condition

$$\frac{V}{v} - \left(\frac{mT}{ME}\right)^{\frac{1}{2}} \gg 1 \qquad \text{or} \qquad T \gg E\frac{M}{m}.$$

Here M and m are respectively the masses of the moving particle and the electron.

In order that this condition shall be satisfied for all electrons in the atom, it is necessary (and sufficient) that it is satisfied for the most closely bound, or K, electrons. It is most easily satisfied in the lightest media, such as for protons (where $M/m \sim 2000$) moving in helium, oxygen, silver and gold ($E = 24$ ev, 527 ev, 25·5 kev, 81 kev), the condition of validity being

$$T \gg 50 \text{ kev, } 1 \text{ Mev, } 50 \text{ Mev, } 160 \text{ Mev.}$$

Actually the theoretical conditions we have imposed are too severe, and the formula can be applied over a much wider range than indicated here. It has been possible to calculate the corrections necessary to make the Bethe expression valid at very low velocities[1].

The correction for the case where the velocity condition is not fulfilled by the K electrons consists in adding to the bracketed term in expression (2) the term $-(C_k/Z)$ so that we get

$$S(\text{Mev.sq.cm.}) = 0{\cdot}510\times 10^{-24} Zz^2 \frac{1}{\beta^2} \times \left[\log\frac{2mc^2}{I} + \log\frac{\beta^2}{1-\beta^2} - \beta^2 - \frac{C_k}{Z}\right]. \tag{4}$$

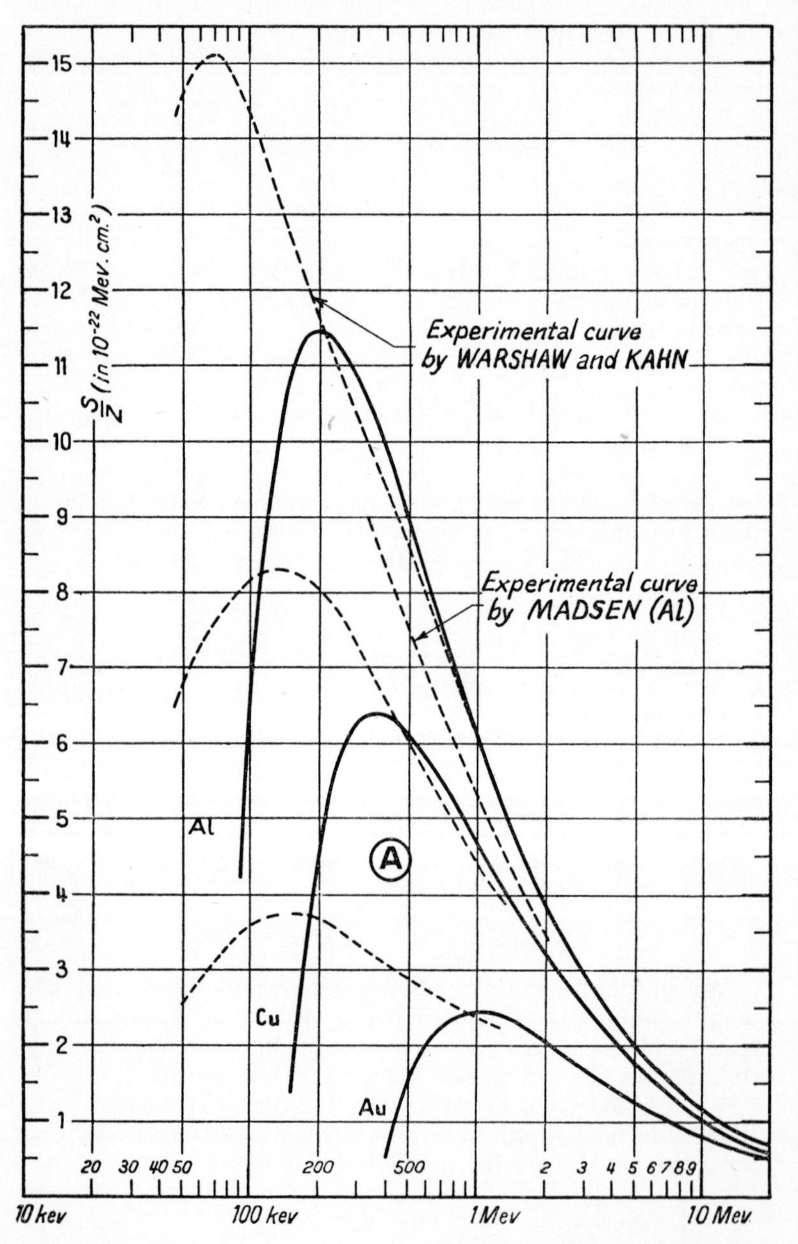

FIG. 15.—Variation in decelerating pow

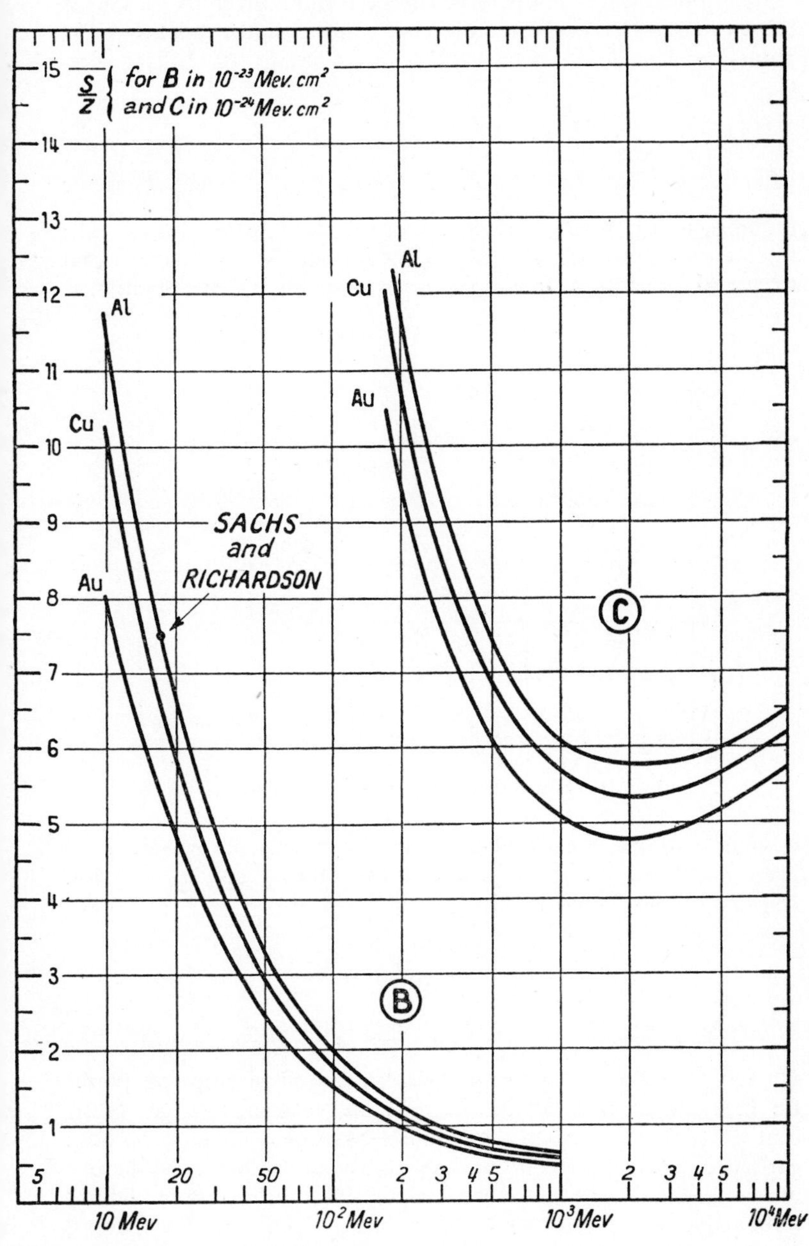

r protons as a function of energy.

C_k is a function of the particle energy T and is given by the curves shown in Fig. 16, where the abscissa is not T but a function of T, namely x, where

$$x = \frac{M}{m}(Z-0\cdot 3)^2 \frac{13\cdot 5}{T} \text{ (ev)}, \tag{5}$$

which differs but slightly from the quantity $\frac{M}{m}\frac{E_k}{T}$, where E_k is the binding energy of the K electrons of the decelerating atoms. The three curves apply to cases of stopping atoms with Z values equal to 10, 30 and 90. As the variation is only slight, extrapolation is

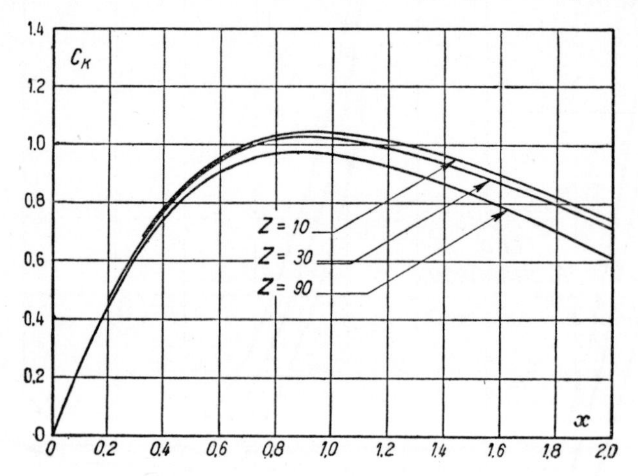

FIG. 16.—Correction to stopping at low velocities.

possible without considerable error. Analogous corrections have been calculated for the case where the velocity condition is not satisfied by the L level electrons:

$$T \lesssim \frac{M}{m} E_L.$$

(5) EXPERIMENTAL MEASUREMENT OF STOPPING POWER

Up to the present, experimental determination of stopping power for light atomic particles has been limited to energy ranges below that where theory predicts a minimum. Such experiments have been carried out chiefly with protons up to about 300 Mev. Numerous measurements have been done on α-particles, but mainly on natural radioactive α-particles, so that the energy limit has been about 10 Mev. Only very few measurements have been done with deuterons, and even more rare are those with other light particles.

Although the various measurements have shown considerable

variation in detail, the principles underlying them have been but few, and we may restrict ourselves to a discussion of some of the general characters.

(a) *Direct Measurement of Energy Loss across a Thin Absorber*

A bundle of particles of fixed energy T_0 strikes normally a thin absorbing foil of thickness Δx. The average energy after traversing the foil will be T_1 which can be measured. Thus the loss of energy is $\Delta T = T_0 - T_1$ and the stopping power is $\Delta T/\Delta x$. There have been various modifications of this idea, differing in the method of measuring T_0 and T_1.

Most often the particles used are those issuing from an accelerator and crossing a magnetic or electric field which serves as analyser, allowing only those particles to pass which have a kinetic energy close to T_0. Beyond the absorber is another analyser for the determination of T_1.

The same method can be applied to the stopping power of gaseous media. In this case the beam traverses a chamber of length l, generally some 10 cm., with an entry window and an exit window formed by foils as thin as possible and of suitable material. T_0 is then the mean energy of the particles having passed the evacuated chamber, and T_1 the corresponding figure when the chamber is filled with the gaseous medium at a carefully-measured pressure.

This method has been applied to α-particles from natural radioactive elements, the energy T_0 of which is well known from spectrometry.

Mention must be made of the method used by Phillips[2] in his study of the stopping power of a gas towards low-energy protons (10–80 kev). The energy T_0 is determined by the potential difference V_0 over which the protons have been accelerated. The beam after passing a certain thickness of the gaseous medium has only the average kinetic energy $T_0 - \Delta T$, and one measures the potential difference $(V_0 - \Delta V)$ required to bring the protons to rest. For protons, singly-charged particles, ΔT in ev is expressed by the same number as ΔV in volts.

(b) *Measurement of Constant Exit Energy*

This type of measurement recalls to mind the fact that it is possible to characterize certain energies of light atomic particles by the fact that they give rise to nuclear reactions of the resonance type.

For example, if one bombards a thin aluminium foil with protons of well-defined energy, these can become captured by the aluminium nuclei, but only at certain clearly defined energies. This probability of capture can be represented as a function of the proton energy by means of an effective captive cross-section, the variation of which is shown in Fig. 17 for protons impinging on aluminium. Each time a proton is captured, γ-rays are emitted, and by the use of a γ-ray detector their intensity can be measured as a function of the proton energy, and this varies as the effective captive cross-section.

The principle of the measurement is as follows. The particles used are supplied by an accelerator, allowing the energy to be varied and readily measured. Measurements of this type have been carried out by the Copenhagen group[3] using a Van de Graaff generator. If the energy is varied around the resonance peak, the detector near the

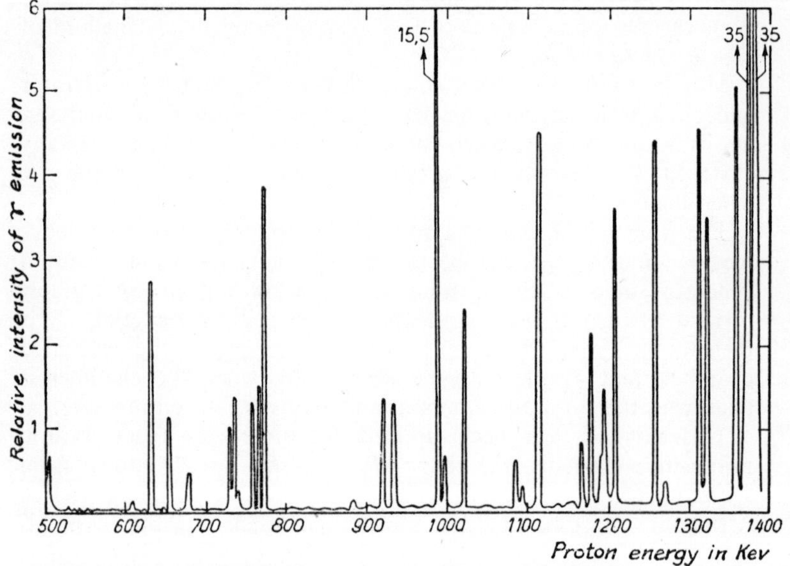

FIG. 17.—Resonance of proton capture in aluminium.

thin bombarded source will show a response of the type shown in Fig. 18(*a*), which refers to the resonance of 986 kev protons on aluminium as observed by the Danes.

If one now interposes in the beam an absorber in which a certain energy loss can take place, it is necessary, in order to observe resonance, that the entry energy into this absorber be increased somewhat. Figure 18(*b*) shows, in the case of an interposed beryllium foil of 0·22 mg./sq. cm., how the detector response varies as a function of the energy of the protons leaving the Van de Graaff generator. There is a peak at 1035 kev, indicating that in the foil in question the average energy loss is 49 kev, so that one can deduce that the stopping power is $49/0 \cdot 22 = 223$ kev/mg./sq. cm.

It is to be noted that the peak is somewhat broadened and flattened. This is because not all the protons traversing the beryllium foil undergo the same energy loss and there is a certain fluctuation around the most probable loss.

In the foregoing example, proton energy changes between entry and exit were measured, these being about 1010 kev, and when one varies the chosen peaks one obtains a large number of points of measurement.

This method is limited in applicability to energies of particles for which resonances can be observed, i.e. only a few Mev, but in fact it has been used only for protons of energy below 2 Mev and could be somewhat extended.

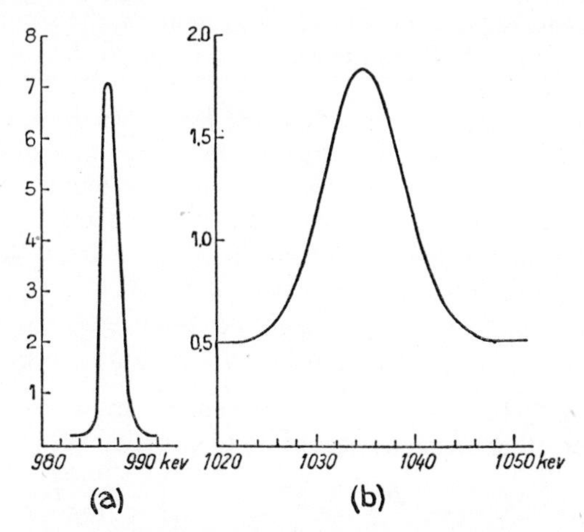

FIG. 18.—Displacement of the resonance ^{27}Al (p, γ) by the insertion of 0·22 mg./sq. cm. of beryllium.

(c) *Measurements of Relative Stopping Power*

These depend upon determination of equivalent absorbing thicknesses. Into a well-defined energized beam of particles, screens of various substances can be interposed, and one measures the thicknesses required to produce the same attenuation of energy. Such energy need not be precisely measured—we need only label it with some figure which can be a fairly sensitive function of the energy, such as the path-length. One must know approximately, then, the initial and final energies in order to know to which energy value the measurement is related.

(6) RESULTS AND APPLICATION OF STOPPING POWER MEASUREMENTS ON PROTONS

As has been seen, the results of measurements available at the moment do not cover completely an extensive energy range for all the various particles and media which one can imagine.

The problem might be posed in another way—are the partial sets of experimental data always in conformity with theory? In the absence of conflicting results, one should be able, provided the theory is on a sound basis, to use the theoretical expressions in order to calculate stopping powers whenever there may be experimental data.

In order to make use of theoretical expressions one must know the I values to introduce into the formula used, and this is done by measuring at some well-defined energy value the stopping power in the medium under consideration. For this purpose one should choose an energy value sufficiently high that C_k becomes negligible. The best value at present conforming to this condition is that of Sachs and Richardson[4], who measured for aluminium the stopping power towards protons of 18-Mev energy, and deduced the value of I_{Al} as 168 ev.

From this value one can deduce the figure for other elements by the simple method of equivalent stopping powers. From such values in the case of 300-Mev protons, obtained by Bakker and Segre[5], the following figures were deduced for q, which may be defined as the stopping power per electron in the atom of the medium, using aluminium as the reference element:

	H	Li	Be	C	Al	Fe	Cu	Ag	Sn	W	Pb	U
$q =$	1·280	1·184	1·113	1·084	1·000	0·941	0·924	0·873	0·859	0·814	0·804	0·786

The value I_{Al} being known, and taken as 168 ev, we can deduce the I values for other elements according to equation (2):

$$q = \frac{\log\frac{2mc^2}{I} + \log\frac{\beta^2}{1-\beta^2} - \beta^2}{\log\frac{2mc^2}{I_{Al}} + \log\frac{\beta^2}{1-\beta^2} - \beta^2} = 1 + \frac{\log\frac{I_{Al}}{I}}{\log\frac{2mc^2}{I_{Al}} + \log\frac{\beta^2}{1-\beta^2} - \beta^2}.$$

This gives the following results:

	H	Li	Be	C	Al	Fe
$I =$	17·8	38·7	68·0	86·5	168·0	270·0
$I/Z =$	17·8	12·9	17·0	14·4	12·9	10·4

	Cu	Ag	Sn	W	Pb	U
$I =$	308·0	464·0	518·0	744·0	805·0	928·0
$I/Z =$	10·6	9·88	10·35	10·05	9·82	10·10

The values so obtained for I/Z have been expressed as functions of Z in Fig. 19, the curve best fitting the points having been drawn in. It is seen that for values of Z equal to or greater than 35, the I/Z rate is virtually constant, and equal to 10 ev. Below 35, on the other hand, I/Z tends to depart from this value, the derivations being the greater the smaller the value of Z.

It should be noted that on a theoretical basis F. Bloch came to the conclusion that I should be proportional to Z. Experience confirms this result, but only when $Z \geqslant 35$.

It is important to point out that the logarithm of I is involved in the expression for stopping power, so that variations in I produce but little effect on stopping power, or inversely, experimental inaccuracies have a large effect upon the I values deduced. It was found, for example, in the work of Sachs and Richardson that a variation of $\pm$ 15 ev from the value 168 ev produced variations in

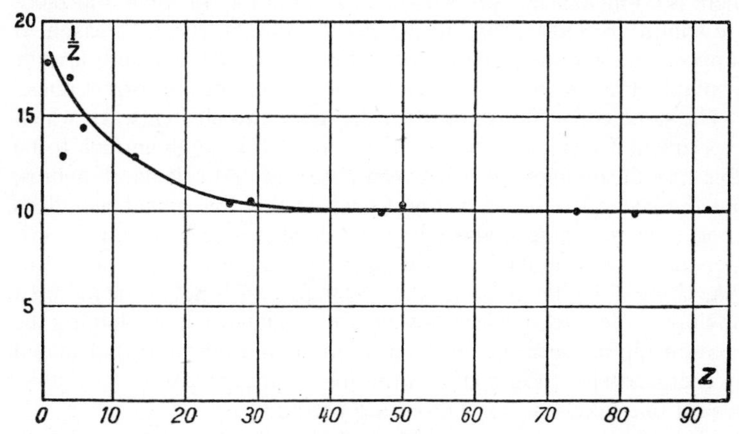

FIG. 19.—Variation of the constant I with atomic number of the medium traversed.

stopping power values to the extent of 1·75 per cent. There is thus no great inaccuracy involved in replacing the I values indicated above by those deduced from the graph.

It is reasonable to expect a regular variation of I as a function of Z for atoms with large numbers of electrons, but in the case of atoms of small atomic number the variations in the binding energies of the less firmly bound electrons as we pass from one atom to another will have their effect upon I. It is probable that the fact that I/Z in the case of lithium is markedly below the curve is not the result of any experimental inaccuracies, but due to the fact that the third electron of lithium is the first of a new level.

On Fig. 15 appear in the curve (full line) the values of the stopping power per electron for aluminium, copper and gold, calculated by means of formula 2, as the proton energy varies from about 100 kev up to about 10^4 Mev. The values of I are $I_{Al} = 168$ ev, $I_{Cu} = 301$ ev, $I_{Au} = 790$ ev.

Upon the same graph (in dotted line) are the results of the

experimental determinations of stopping power for protons in the case of these same three metals, for protons in each case, obtained by Warshaw[6] and Kahn[7], although unfortunately restricted to energies above 1350 kev.

These results differ considerably from the calculated curves, but this is hardly surprising in view of the fact that they relate to a zone of energy where, on the one hand, corrections C_k should be applied, but have been disregarded in the curves, and on the other hand, the effect of the charge on the proton begins to make itself felt.

But the important fact emerges that the experimental curve for aluminium agrees with that calculated from 800 kev onwards. Since there is co-incidence with experimental values at 18 Mev, and there are sound grounds justifying the Bethe formula, there is reason to suppose that within the whole zone where experimental results are not available, the results given by calculation would be the correct ones.

The same conclusions apply for the other two elements, for which experimental results are not available at energies high enough to be able to indicate agreement between observed and calculated figures, but the general trend leads one to expect that agreement would be good. On the same graph (shown in broken lines) are the experimental values obtained by Madsen[3], and these are notably lower than those of Kahn, although the reason for this is not at the moment obvious. There would seem always to be difficulty in explaining the relationship between the results of Madsen and the values calculated at energies where the charge variation of the proton is negligible, even if one takes the correction into account.

Measurements of the stopping powers have also been made with gases, on the one hand between 10 and 80 kev by Phillips[2], and on the other hand up to 600 kev by Weyl[8] and by Reynolds and co-workers[9]. The results of these investigations are shown in Fig. 20, expressed in terms of the stopping power per electron.

It will be noticed that, with the exception of oxygen, which one would expect to give values close to those for air and nitrogen, the results of the two sets of authors agree well.

Shown in the same figure is the curve relating to aluminium, due to Kahn and Warshaw. This curve lies not between those for argon and air, as one might expect, but does tend to that position at higher energies. The reason for this behaviour has not yet been made clear. It seems to indicate that the decelerating power at low energies is dependent in some way upon the density of the medium.

(7) The Case of Light Atomic Particles other than Protons

The Bethe formula tells us that for a given speed β, for the moving particle, the decelerating power depends not upon the nature of the particle, except in so far as Z^2 is involved, and is independent of mass. In particular, the case of isotopes is interesting, for on the one hand they have the same nuclear charge, and on the other hand they should obey the same law of charge variation with velocity during deceleration, the stopping power being expressible by the same expression in terms of β.

The curves shown in Figs. 15 and 20 are thus applicable to deuterons and tritons, provided we consider particles of the same velocity, so that we must multiply by factors of 2 or 3 the energy scales which applied to protons. All measurements so far made have confirmed the validity of this statement.

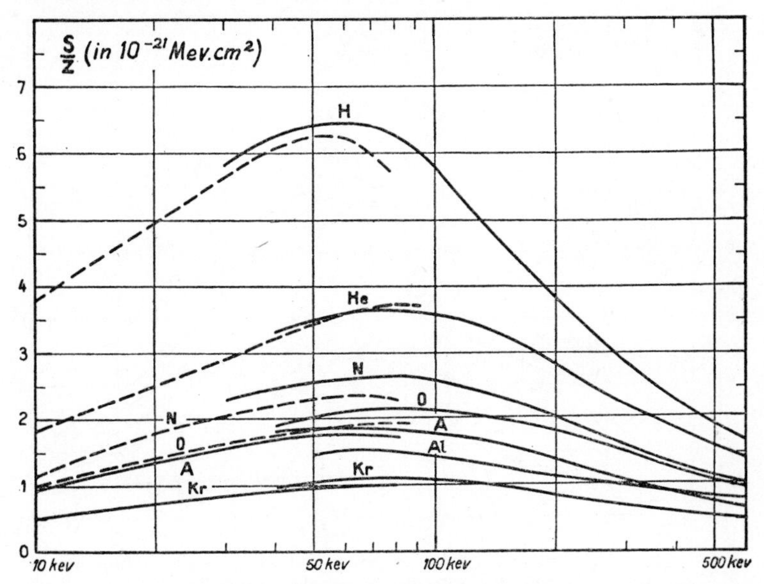

FIG. 20.—Variation in decelerating power for protons in gases as a function of energy, referred to a single electron.

In the case of α-particles, again at equal speed, we should expect the stopping power to be four times that for protons at the same velocities at energies for which the particle is always carrying a double charge, i.e. at energies of some Mev. At low energies the charge variation during slowing down will disturb the applicability of this formula of Bethe.

The principal measurements of the decelerating power for α-particles were made some time ago, and were due to Rosenblum[10] for solid media, and to Mano[11] for gases. They consisted in measuring the function $T(x)$, which represents the energy of the α-particles from thorium C′ ($T_0 = 8\cdot77$ Mev), as a function of the thickness of the material traversed. It was easy to deduce the relationship

$$\frac{S}{Z} = -\frac{1}{nZ}\frac{\mathrm{d}T}{\mathrm{d}x}.$$

The region covered extends approximately up to 2·5 Mev. If we compare the results with those obtained more recently with those for protons, we find that for the elements studied so far, the values of S/Z are, within the limits of experimental accuracy, equal to four times the values applicable to the proton at the same speed, when the kinetic energy is four times smaller. This is just what we should expect from the Bethe formula, since in the region of energy in question, the charge variation of the proton is practically zero and that of the α-particle also very small.

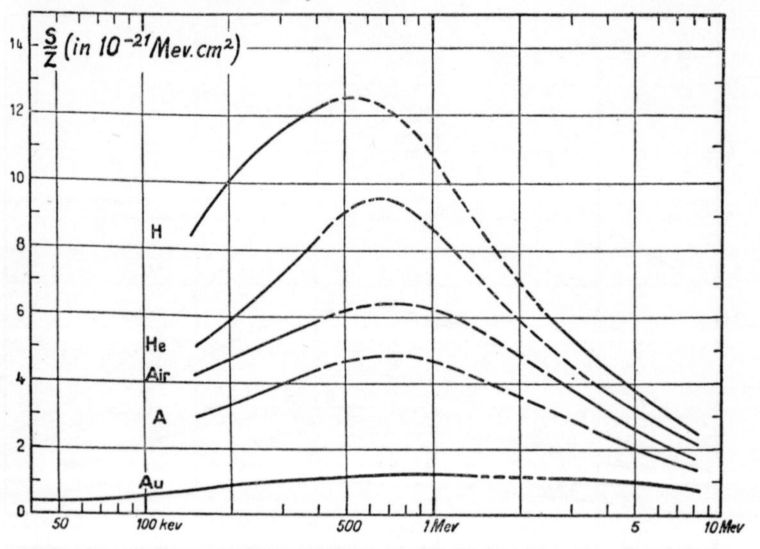

FIG. 21.—Variation in decelerating power for α-particles as a function of energy, referred to a single electron.

At much lower energies, measurements have been made in the case of gases by Weyl, and by Wilcox in gold. The curves shown in Fig. 21 show the results for some of the atoms studied. The dotted portion is an extrapolation between two series of experimental values, and there is hardly any need to emphasize the lack of precision in this portion.

There are very few results relating to light atomic particles of nuclear charge greater than 2, but when they are completely ionized, the Bethe formula becomes applicable. A few measurements between 150 and 400 kev have been carried out by Weyl for ions of nitrogen and neon.

(8) CORRECTION FOR DENSITY AND THE CERENKOV EFFECT

At high energies, the Bethe formula indicates that beyond a certain limit, the slowing-down power increases indefinitely via the logarithmic term, $-\log(1-\beta^2)$.

In fact, a phenomenon which is not taken into consideration in the Bethe formula comes into play at very high energies, and modifies the trend of the variation. We have until now assumed that the different atoms within a medium behave independently, as if in isolation, and that each atom acted upon the moving particle as if the other atoms of the medium were absent. This is not the case, however, especially at very high energies. The passage of a particle acts upon the medium which it traverses, creating in the vicinity of the trajectory an electrical polarization of the medium under the action of the electrical field which is displaced as the particle progresses. This polarization of adjacent atoms in the path of the moving particle results in a decrease in the electric field in the more remote regions of the trajectory and a reduction in the interactions involving energy loss. Such a decrease will be more marked when there are many atoms involved on the track, and so the correction is greater when the medium is a solid one.

Many workers have tried to calculate the corrections which must be applied to the Bethe formula in order to take this phenomenon into account, and there have been many approximations and results from the various authors. Nevertheless, we can say, in a qualitative way, that in condensed media the decrease in the decelerating power is not appreciable until near the minimum, and this is at energies rarely encountered in the case of most atomic particles, except in cosmic rays. However, it can become important in that there is an indefinite growth of the logarithmic term as a function of the energy. The decelerating power, after passing through its minimum for a kinetic energy close to twice the energy equivalent to the rest mass of the particle, appears to increase somewhat and then to reach a constant value which is hardly greater at its maximum. Before assuming certainty on this matter, we must gather together the maximum available amount of experimental data.

In gases, the polarization effect appears to involve no correction in the decelerating power except when the energy of the moving particle exceeds a hundred times the energy equivalent to its rest mass. For atomic particles, this effect appears to be outside the realms of observation.

We find somewhat similar results in the case of electrons, but the energy equivalent to their rest mass is only about 0·5 Mev, so that the phenomenon now appears at energies well within experimental experience.

The polarization effect is a local one and a temporary one, connected with the passage of the particle, and as soon as the particle has passed, the atoms become depolarized. To this depolarization there corresponds an energetic emission from the atoms, which give up the energy they acquired as a result of the polarization.

At each point of the trajectory, then, and at the moment of the presence of the passing particle, there is an electromagnetic radiation due to depolarization. If the speed of the particle is greater than that of light in the medium under consideration, the collection of emissions will be in phase and gives rise to a resultant conical wave with the particle at the summit (Fig. 22), analogous to the conical ballistic wave which accompanies the displacement of a projectile in air when its speed is greater than the velocity of sound. This electromagnetic radiation is called the Cerenkov effect[12], after the first observer, although the theory of this was developed by Frank and Tamm[13].

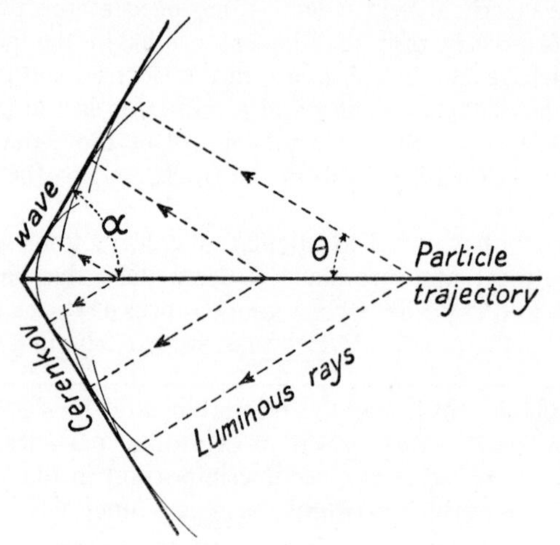

FIG. 22.—Emission of Cerenkov radiation.

It may be said that the half-angle at the summit of the cone of electromagnetic field is given by

$$\sin\alpha = \frac{v_0}{v} = \frac{c}{nv} = \frac{1}{n\beta},$$

where v_0 and v are respectively the speed of light and that of the particle in the medium, and n is the refractive index of the latter.

This theory indicates that the spectrum of the frequency of the radiation is such that, for each cm. of the trajectory, the number of quanta emitted with a frequency between ν and $\nu+d\nu$ equals

$$N(\nu)\,d\nu = \frac{4\pi^2 z^2 e^2}{hc^2}\left(1-\frac{1}{n^2\beta^2}\right)d\nu.$$

In a non-dispersive medium (in which n is independent of ν) the number of quanta per unit of frequency is constant, and as each is carrying an energy $h\nu$, the radiated energy per unit frequency must be proportional to the frequency. In a medium transparent to light, it will be mainly the violet and ultra-violet which will be observed. In a dispersive medium, the growth of n with ν will tend to favour the higher frequencies.

The application of the preceding formula, which can be written as

$$N(\nu)\mathrm{d}\nu = 15\cdot 2\times 10^{-13} Z^2\left(1-\frac{1}{n^2\beta^2}\right)\mathrm{d}\nu,$$

indicates that a particle with unit charge, with a velocity close to that of light *in vacuo*, circulating in a medium of refractive index $n = 1\cdot 6$, will emit about 300 photons in the visible spectrum per cm. of its track.

The loss of energy corresponding to this emission is only a small portion of the energy lost by the particle during its slowing down (about 0·1 per cent), but the emission is luminous and readily visible to an observer.

The luminous rays are emitted in directions making an angle θ given by

$$\cos\theta = \frac{1}{n\beta}$$

with the direction of the particle, and this angle is a function of the speed βc of the latter. This makes it possible, by means of optical instruments of great precision, to measure θ and hence to find β. Thus, for example, Mather[14] set up an apparatus which was able to measure to within 0·8 Mev the kinetic energy of protons up to 340 Mev.

REFERENCES

1. WALSKE, M. C. (1952), *Phys. Rev.*, **88,** 1283.
2. PHILLIPS, J. A. (1953), *Phys. Rev.*, **90,** 532.
3. MADSEN, C. B. (1953), *K. danske vidensk. Selsk.*, **27,** 13.
4. SACHS, D. C., and RICHARDSON, J. R. (1951), *Phys. Rev.*, **83,** 834, and (1953), **89,** 1163.
5. BAKKER, C. J., and SEGRE, E. (1951), *Phys. Rev.*, **81,** 489.
6. WARSHAW, S. D. (1949), *Phys. Rev.*, **76,** 1759.
7. KAHN, D. (1953), *Phys. Rev.*, **90,** 503.
8. WEYL, P. K. (1953), *Phys. Rev.*, **91,** 289.
9. REYNOLDS, H. K., DUNBAR, D. N. F., WANXEL, W. A., and WHALING, W. (1953), *Phys. Rev.*, **92,** 742.
10. ROSENBLUM, S. (1928), *Ann. Phys., Paris*, **10,** 408.
11. MANO, G. (1934), *Ann. Phys., Paris*, **1,** 407.
12. CERENKOV, P. A. (1937), *Phys. Rev.*, **52,** 378.
13. FRANK, I. M., and TAMM, I. E. (1937), *C. R. Acad. Sci. U.R.S.S.*, **14,** 109.
14. MATHER, R. L. (1951), *Phys. Rev.*, **84,** 181.

Chapter 6

IONIZATION BY MOVING PARTICLES

(1) Specific Ionization and Decelerating Power

If a particle be considered as moving within some material medium, the loss of energy within an element of length Δx in the path is

$$\Delta T = R\Delta x,$$

where R is the stopping power of the medium traversed, varying with the energy of the particle. The portion of the energy lost in this way is utilized in ionizing the medium. Let ΔI be the number of ion-pairs produced within the same element Δx. Then the specific ionization is given by $J = \Delta T/\Delta x$ representing the number of ion-pairs created in unit length of the path. J is obviously a function of the energy of the ionizing particle. Often we make use of the quantity

$$w = \frac{R}{J} = \frac{\Delta T}{\Delta I}$$

which is the mean energy loss per pair of ions formed. Since w is the quotient of two quantities which depend on the particle energy, it is itself dependent on the energy. However, this dependence, when it exists at all, is so small that we can say that within wide limits w is independent of the energy of the particle and even of its nature. Thus it becomes only a characteristic of the medium.

This result signifies that when a charged particle is slowed down in passing through a medium, the portion of its energy which is lost in ion-pair formation represents a constant fraction of the total energy loss.

In actuality the constancy of w can be considered as only very approximately established. From the theoretical point of view, Fano has shown that one would expect approximate constancy, but this theory has not been extended to the point where one can say definitely that complete constancy should result.

On the experimental side, the only accurate measurements made so far have been those of Jesse and Sadauskis, which permit only partial conclusions to be reached. These measurements have given values not for $w = \Delta T/\Delta I$, but for $W = T/I$, or the total kinetic energy T divided by the number of ion-pairs I created in a gas when all the energy of the particle is given up.

The principle underlying these measurements is to arrange in an ionization chamber a radioactive source which is emitting α-particles of well-defined energies, the chamber having a shape and dimensions such that the complete path of the particles is retained within the chamber. When an α-particle creates I ion-pairs within the gas used to fill the chamber, the positive ions are collected by the negative electrode, and the negative ions by the positive electrode, so that between the two electrodes is established a potential difference which changes the applied potential by an amount

$$\Delta V = \frac{Ie}{C},$$

where e is the elementary charge and C the capacity of the chamber and its associated circuitry. This potential change is amplified, and measured by some suitable instrumentation. If the capacity C is also measured, then I can be deduced.

In the following table are given figures by Jesse and Sadauskis[1] for the quotient $W = T/I$ applying to the kinetic energy of the particles from polonium and the number of ion-pairs produced in various gases when this energy is completely absorbed, together with the corresponding I numbers:

	He	Ne	A	Kr
W (ev per ion-pair) =	42·7	36·8	26·4	24·1
I (in thousands of ion-pairs) =	124·0	144·0	200·0	220·0

	Xe	H_2	CO_2	Air	O_2
W =	21·9	36·3	34·5	35·5	32·5
I =	242·0	146·0	154·0	149·0	163·0

	N_2	CH_4	C_2H_2	C_2H_6	C_2H_4
W =	36·6	29·2	27·5	26·6	28·0
I =	145·0	182·0	193·0	199·0	189·0

It should be noted that the measured values are very sensitive to the degree of purity of the gas, especially in the case of helium and neon, for which the values of W given above, and obtained with highly purified gases, are greater than those obtained previously by other workers.

Jesse and Sadauskis[2] have shown that the addition of small amounts of argon to other inert gases produces the following effects:

	I	W
Helium of maximum purity	128,300	41·3 ev
,, with 0·13 per cent of argon, by volume	178,400	29·7 ev
Neon of maximum purity	146,000	36·3 ev
,, with 0·12 per cent of argon, by volume	203,000	26·1 ev

It should be stated here that the figures given by the same two workers in 1953 and 1952 for helium and neon in the pure state are slightly different. This perhaps means that their purification techniques have been improved.

According to Bortner and Hurst[3], who found, for the other gases studied, the same values as those obtained by Jesse and Sadauskis, the value of W should be greater than 42·7, as they found a figure of 46 ev.

These figures merely indicate the necessity for extreme care in the purification of the gases used if the values obtained are to be of value. The explanation of the variations found in the case of helium is perhaps that certain helium atoms may be excited by the passage of an α-particle into a metastable state for which the excitation energy is 19·8 ev. The atom thus excited may strike an argon atom, to which its excitation energy is transferred, and as this energy exceeds the energy of 15·7 ev required for ionization, the argon atom becomes ionized.

In order to establish to what degree the value of W might be considered as independent of T, Jesse and Sadauskis[4] measured the ionization I produced in argon by α-particles from various radioactive elements, of energies between 5·298 Mev (for Po) and 8·812 Mev (ThC′), and have shown that W is constant to well within 0·5 per cent. In a similar way they have shown that the same relationship holds for α-particles derived from nuclear reactions induced by thermal neutrons, such as $^{6}Li(n, \alpha)^{3}H$ and $^{10}B(n, \alpha)^{7}Li$, with kinetic energies respectively 2·060 and 1·474 Mev, as well as for the lithium ions of energy 0·841 Mev produced in this last reaction.

We may thus conclude that in the case of argon gas, the values of W and w are constant for α-particles at least up to 9 Mev.

On the other hand, if instead of argon, air is considered, the same authors have shown that within the same range of energies, the value of W varied by several per cent.

It is reasonable, then, to assume that to a first approximation w is constant and characteristic of the medium in which the particles are moving, but independent of the velocity and nature of these particles. It must be realized, however, that this conclusion is not conclusively established, and that deviations may yet be demonstrated.

This constancy of w means that the variation of the specific ionization with energy is proportional to the change in stopping power of a medium, according to the expression

$$w = \frac{\mathrm{d}T/\mathrm{d}x}{\mathrm{d}J/\mathrm{d}x}.$$

(2) Bragg Curves

In the preceding paragraph the specific ionization was defined as the number of ion-pairs formed per unit length of trajectory by a single moving particle. It often happens in practice, however, that one is obliged to measure not the number of ions produced by a single moving particle, but by a whole bundle of particles of such density that the effects of individual particles cannot be separated one from the other. This is the case with the α-particles emitted by an intense

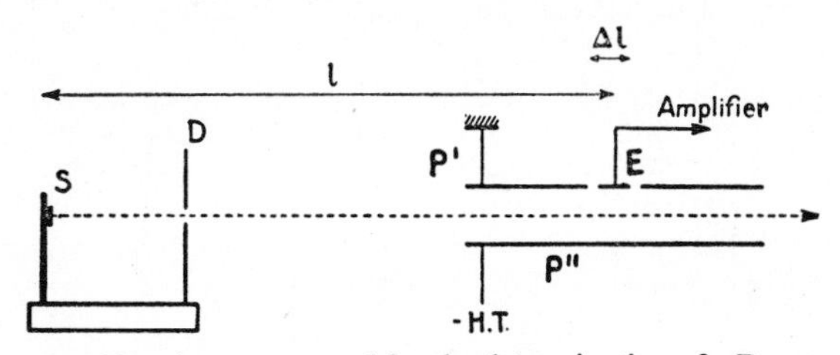

Fig. 23.—Apparatus used for the determination of a Bragg curve.

radioactive source or with the particles forming the beam issuing from a particle accelerator.

We give the name Bragg curve to the graph which gives the relative ionization value along a bundle of particles having all the same original velocity and direction. As abscissæ we take the distances from the origin at which the measurements are taken, and as ordinates we take a quantity proportional to the number of ion-pairs formed per unit length of the path of the bundle.

Many workers have studied Bragg curves, especially those for the particles in air. Various experimental devices have been utilized. Fig. 23 shows one of these.

In an airtight receiver a point source S and a diaphragm D give rise to a narrow pencil of α-particles which pass between the two plates P′ and P″ to the ionization chamber. A portion E, small in size, of the plate P′ is insulated, and forms the electrode which collects the ions formed in a small section of the path Δl. Into the receiver is introduced a given gas at known pressure, and the current collected on E is measured while the distance between S and E is made to vary. Such measurements reveal the number ΔI of ion-pairs formed in given time within the length Δl after the trajectory l has been made. If I is the number of ion-pairs formed during the trajectory l after emission, and dl is small, we can say

$$\frac{\Delta I}{\Delta l} = \frac{dI}{dl}.$$

The Bragg curve is characterized by a very marked maximum followed by a sudden drop to zero. Fig. 24 shows the Bragg curves for the α-particles from polonium ($v = 1 \cdot 597 \times 10^9$ cm./sec., and $E = 5 \cdot 300$ Mev), and for those from RaC′ ($v = 1 \cdot 922 \times 10^9$ cm./sec., and $E = 7 \cdot 683$ Mev) in air under normal conditions. It is usual to represent these Bragg curves with arbitrary ordinates so chosen that the maximum on the ordinate will be unity.

From these curves it will be seen that the distance at which the ionization becomes zero is somewhat ill-defined. For this reason it

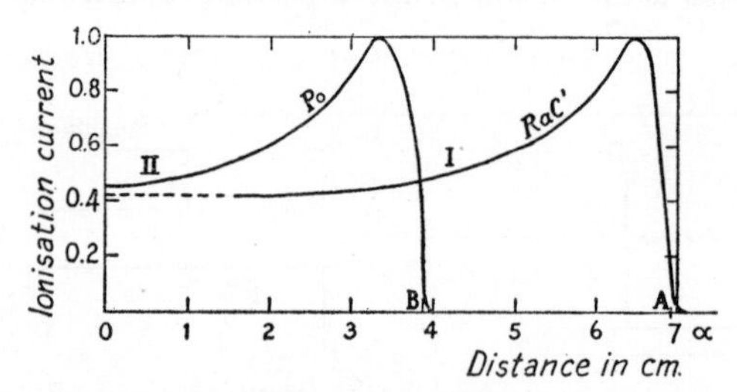

FIG. 24.—Bragg curves for polonium and RaC′.

is customary to define the length of path of α-particles not by the point at which the ionizing power dI/dl becomes zero, but in the following way. The descending part of the Bragg curve shows a point of inflexion, and is practically linear for a great part of its length. If this linear portion is extrapolated on to the abscissa axis, one obtains a characteristic length of path for the α-particles of given energy, which we call the extrapolated path. This can be defined with considerable exactitude, i.e. to within 10^{-3} cm. This extrapolated path is about 1 mm. smaller than the length of path at which the Bragg curve meets the abscissa axis. The following are some values of this extrapolated path for the α-particles from a number of radioactive elements in air:

Element:	Po	RaA	ThA	RaC′	ThC′	
Energy:	5·303	5·998	6·774	7·680	8·776	Mev
Extrapolated path:	38·70	46·85	56·72	68·53	86·16	mm.

It should be noted that Bragg curves corresponding to different energies for the same type of particle are not completely and accurately superimposable, especially at the terminal part of the curve. As

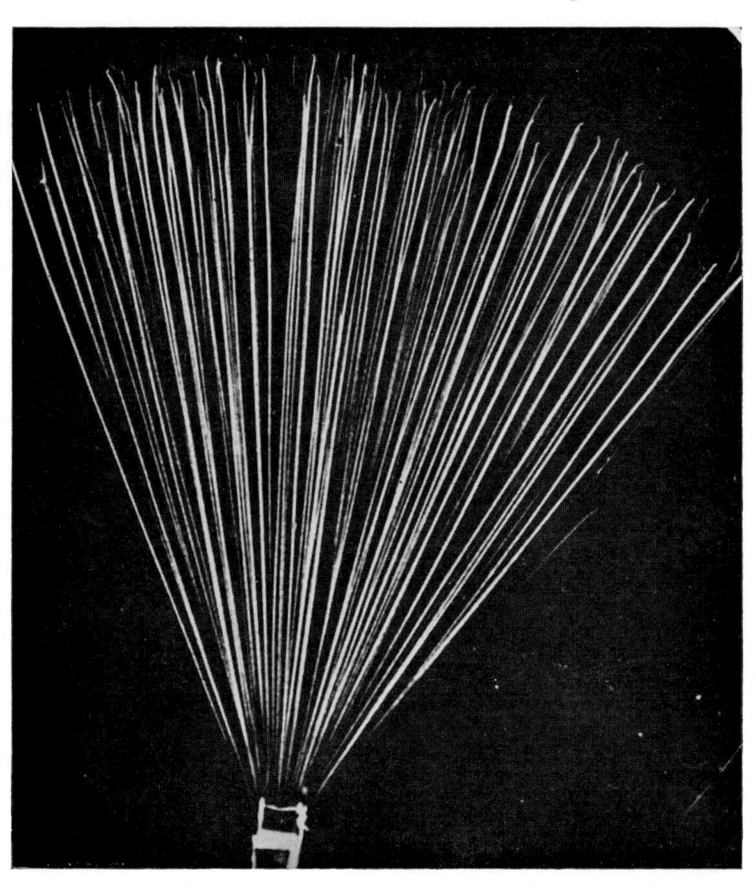

FIG. 25.—Tracks of monokinetic particles.

Fig. 26.—Tracks of α-particles of two energies, from RaA and RaC′.

will be seen in the next chapter, this is related to the existence of a path fluctuation.

In order to express in absolute values the ordinates of a Bragg curve, it should be noted that the area enclosed by the curve equals the product of the number of particles which have contributed to the measured ionization and the total number of ion-pairs created per particle. In calculating these results for a single particle it is to be noted that the maximum on the Bragg curves for air corresponds to about 6,500 ion-pairs per mm. at 15°C and 760 mm. Hg pressure in the case of α-particles.

(3) Electrostatic Unit of Polonium

The measure of total ionization produced in normal air by the particles from a radioactive element is often used as a measure of the quantity of that radio-element.

For example, 1 millicurie of polonium emits $3{\cdot}7\times10^7$ α-particles each second, and in the type of ionization chamber described above this will give rise to

$$\tfrac{1}{2}\times3{\cdot}7\times10^7\times150{,}000 = 278\times10^{10} \text{ ion-pairs per sec.}$$

This corresponds to an ionization current of

$$4{\cdot}80\times10^{-10}\times278\times10^{10} = 1{,}330 \text{ e.s.u.}$$

Thus the electrostatic unit (1 e.s.u.) of polonium corresponds to 0·75 microcurie of that element.

REFERENCES

1. Jesse, W. P., and Sadauskis, J. (1953), *Phys. Rev.*, **90**, 1120.
2. Jesse, W. P., and Sadauskis, J. (1952), *Phys. Rev.*, **88**, 417.
3. Bortner, T. E., and Hurst, G. S. (1953), *Phys. Rev.*, **90**, 160.
4. Jesse, W. P., and Sadauskis, J. (1950), *Phys. Rev.*, **77**, 782.

Chapter 7

THE PATH OF LIGHT ATOMIC PARTICLES

(1) Mean Path and Path Fluctuation

Various experiments have demonstrated the concept of the path of a particle, and one of the most convincing involves photographing the tracks left in the Wilson cloud chamber by the α-particles emitted by a radioactive source of such intensity that a large number of tracks may be observed upon a single exposure. If the source approaches point dimensions, and if the tracks are limited by means of a diaphragm that allows the passage of particles which are travelling in a definite plane, we see that the extremities of the tracks, i.e. the points where the particles have too little energy to cause any ionization of the medium, are arranged fairly well in the arc of a circle centred on the source (Fig. 25). Thus, it might be said that all particles emitted initially with the same energy lose their total energy at the same distance from the source in a given gaseous medium. Hence, the path depends on the energy of emission. Fig. 26 shows a similar photograph, but obtained with RaA in equilibrium with its derivative RaC′, so that there are emitted two groups of α-particles with energies of 5·998 Mev and 7·680 Mev respectively. The two sets of tracks are clearly seen, the shorter ones corresponding to the particles from the RaA, and the longer ones to those from RaC′.

In actual fact, closer inspection shows that there are slight differences in track lengths, so that it is not possible to attribute the same energy to every particle from a given source.

If instead of considering a single particle, we consider a collection of N identical particles, we can trace the curve which gives the proportion $\mathrm{d}N/N$ of these particles for which the end of the track is between distances of l and $l+\mathrm{d}l$ from the origin (Fig. 27). This curve presents a bell-shaped line with an axis of symmetry at the abscissa P. The distance P is then called the mean free path of the particle in question, for the given energy and the given medium. This mean path might also be defined by the fact that 50 per cent of the particles have a track shorter than this distance, and 50 per cent of them have a longer track.

This curve, giving the distribution of tracks, might also be fairly accurately represented by the gaussian formula

$$\frac{\mathrm{d}N}{N} = \frac{1}{\sqrt{\pi}} \mathrm{e}^{-(\epsilon^2/\alpha^2)} \frac{\mathrm{d}\epsilon}{\alpha},$$

where ϵ is the deviation $l-P$ of the actual path from the mean path, and α is a constant characteristic of the particles considered, and of their energy and the stopping medium. This α is known as the path fluctuation parameter.

The preceding formula might also give the probability $d\varpi_\epsilon = dN/N$ of the particle having a deviation from the mean track lying between the limits ϵ and $\epsilon + d\epsilon$.

Instead of taking this elementary probability into consideration, we might also concern ourselves with the integral probability, or the probability of the track being greater than the given value l. This is given by

$$\varpi = \int_{l-P}^{\infty} d\varpi_\epsilon.$$

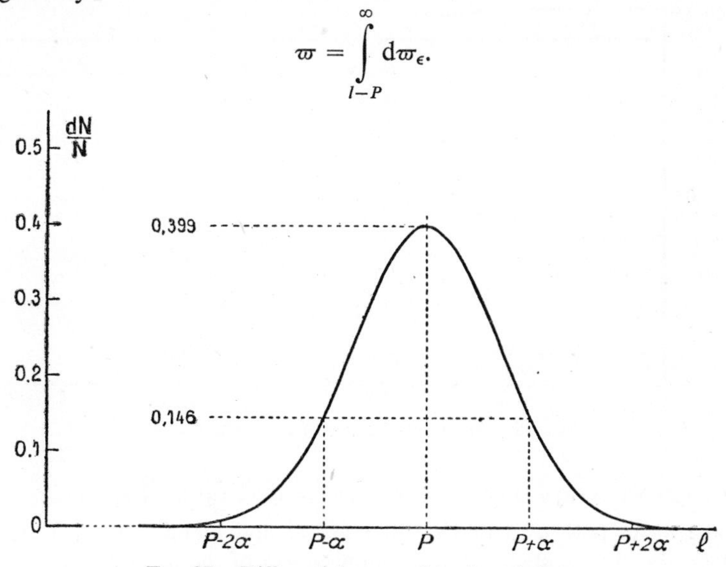

FIG. 27.—Differential curve of track variations.

Fig. 28 shows this function of l, which is obviously zero when $l \gg P$, and unity when $l \ll P$. It should be noted that the values are 0·92 and 0·08 when $P-\alpha$ and $P+\alpha$ are the l values respectively, giving physical significance to the path fluctuation parameter, which is thus the deviation value which has a 16 per cent chance of being exceeded in the absolute value. We might also say that if we consider a great number of particles, 84 per cent of these will have a path differing in length from P by less than α in absolute value.

The track fluctuation parameter is always small compared with the mean path, and it is this which makes the latter so interesting. For example, in the case of the α-particles from polonium, with an energy of 5·300 Mev in air at 15°C and at one atmosphere pressure, $P = 38{\cdot}42$ mm. and $\alpha = 0{\cdot}62$ mm.

A knowledge of the relation between energy and mean path for the various types of particles in common media is of importance in order to forecast the behaviour of given particles and for the deduction of the value of the energy value of a given particle from observation of the path length. In principle, this latter is only possible from the mean path, working on a given group of identical particles. Even if we work with a single isolated particle the relative smallness of α when compared with P results in an error which is almost negligible when we calculate the real path from the mean path. Thus 'track' may often replace 'mean track'.

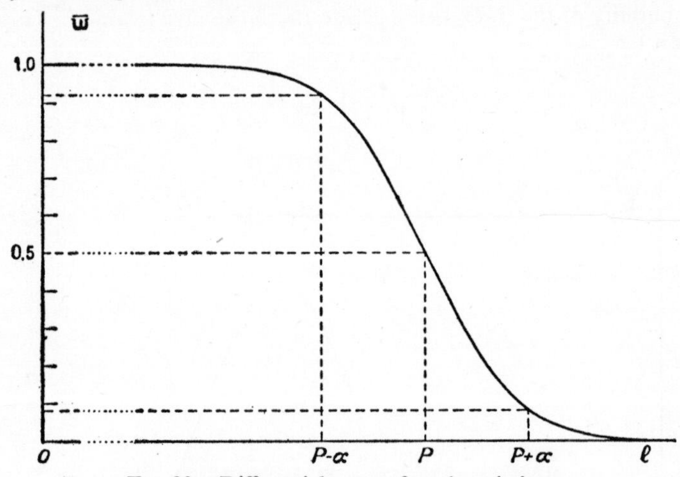

FIG. 28.—Differential curve of track variations.

(2) Relation between Mean Paths of Various Particles

The mean path of a particle of mass M and kinetic energy T (for velocity v) is related to the stopping power of the medium by

$$P = \int_T^0 \mathrm{d}x = \int_0^T \frac{\mathrm{d}T}{(-\mathrm{d}T/\mathrm{d}x)} = \int_0^T \frac{\mathrm{d}T}{R} = \int_0^v \frac{Mg(v)}{R}\mathrm{d}v$$

and also

$$\frac{\mathrm{d}T}{\mathrm{d}v} = Mg(v).$$

In velocity ranges where the Bethe formula holds, i.e. when $v > v_0$, R has the form

$$R = Z^2 f(v),$$

an expression which depends only on the velocity, the nature of the particle not being involved except in so far as its atomic number Z is concerned. Thus we can write

$$P = \int_0^{v_0} \frac{Mg(v)}{R}\cdot\mathrm{d}v + \int_{v_0}^{v} \frac{M}{Z^2}\cdot\frac{g(v)}{f(v)}\cdot\mathrm{d}v = P(v_0) + \frac{M}{Z^2}\int_{v_0}^{v} \frac{g(v)}{f(v)}\cdot\mathrm{d}v.$$

Now suppose we wish to compare the paths of two particles which are isotopic, such as the proton and the deuteron. We know that the stopping power, even for low energies where the Bethe formula is not valid, depends only on the speed of the particle. Hence we deduce

$$P = M\int_0^v \frac{g(v)}{R(v)}\,dv = M\phi(v).$$

In other words, at equal velocity, the paths of isotopic particles are proportional to their masses. For example, a proton, a deuteron, and a triton, assumed to have equal speeds, and hence having energies in the ratios 1, 2, 3, will also have paths related by the ratio 1:2:3.

If we now compare non-isotopic atomic particles, we know that the stopping powers are proportional to Z^2, but the law of variation of Z^2 with velocity is not the same for these particles, so that we cannot establish any valid comparison unless charges are constant. If v_0 is the smallest velocity for which, in the case of the particles being compared, the Bethe formula can no longer be applied, we can say, if we use 1 and 2 for the relative sizes of the particles, that

$$P_1(v) = P_1(v_0)+\frac{M_1}{(Z_1)^2}\phi(v) \qquad P_2(v) = P_2(v_0)+\frac{M_2}{(Z_2)^2}\phi(v) \qquad v > v_0.$$

Hence we obtain

$$P_2(v) = \frac{M_2}{(Z_2)^2}\cdot\frac{(Z_1)^2}{M_1}\cdot P_1(v)+A,$$

where A is a constant characteristic for the two particles compared and for the medium through which they pass, and independent of speed.

If now we compare, for example, α-particles and protons, then the speed v_0 will be that corresponding to α-particles of 2·4 Mev and protons of 0·6 Mev, since at these speeds the stopping powers will be still proportional to Z^2. Above v_0, then, it is only necessary to know the path-energy relationship for one particle to be able to calculate that of the other, the constant A being determined by measuring simultaneously P_1 and P_2 for a given velocity.

As the energies considered become markedly greater than $\frac{1}{2}mv_0^2$, the correction term A becomes rapidly negligible, and we can often say with justification that at equal velocities the paths are proportional to the masses and inversely proportional to the squares of the charges. In the particular cases of α-particles and protons, the ratios M/Z^2 are, to a first approximation, equal, so that we may also say that at equal velocities the α-particle and the proton have equal paths. More accurately, we should take into consideration the fact that the mass of the α-particle is not exactly four times that of the proton, so that we can put

$$P_p(T) = 1 \cdot 007 P_\alpha(3 \cdot 97 T) + A.$$

In air at 15°C and 760 mm. Hg pressure, the constant A is equal to -2 mm. This represents 10 per cent of the path of 0·9 Mev protons and 3·6 Mev α-particles, and about 1 per cent of the path of 3·65 Mev protons and 14·6 Mev α-particles.

At low energies, when the charge change phenomena make impossible any comparisons between non-isotopic particles, experimental determinations should be made at least for one representative of a family of isotopes.

The preceding considerations have shown us that, as far as large energies are concerned, a knowledge of the path-energy relationships for one type of particle involves a knowledge of the same sort of relationship for other particles. On the other hand the curve may also be calculated from the Bethe formula, which applies fairly accurately to stopping power. Experimental measurements at high energies, then, are essentially a test of the accuracy and validity of the Bethe formula or of the correct choice of the constant I.

At low energies, however, if we wish to calculate the path-energy relationships by integration of the stopping power, we shall need experimental values of the stopping power. It is usually more accurate, however, to make direct measurement of the average path at various energies. Once the energy-path relationship is established, one can derive the stopping power as a function of energy.

The establishment of the path-energy relationship for a given medium and for a given type of particle is possible by means of the data obtained from direct measurements, from indirect measurements on paths in the same medium for other particles or by the integration of the stopping power, and from calculated values.

(3) Mean Path and Extrapolated Path

We now have two distinct methods by which we may define the path of particles of definite energy, and in both cases we presuppose that we are dealing with a bundle of particles travelling parallel with one another in a fixed direction.

In the first case we find the proportion of the particles of the bundle which travel beyond a certain distance, and then we draw a number-distance curve of the type shown in Fig. 28. The mean path is then the abscissa corresponding to the ordinate at 0·5.

In the second case we study how the ionization per unit length of path varies along the length of the path, and then draw the Bragg curve, from which we deduce the extrapolated path, as mentioned in Chapter 6.

What relationship exists between these two paths?

When a particle arrives at the end of its path, its ionization varies according to a very definite law, the establishment of which will be outlined later. For example, in air (at 15°C and 760 mm. Hg), Holloway and Livingston found that the ionization curve for a particle is as shown in Fig. 29. This curve, while showing the same general trend, does actually differ from a Bragg curve, the main point of difference being that it does not join tangentially the distance axis, but tends towards zero perpendicularly to this axis. Let us use $i(r)$ to denote ionization at a distance r from the end of the trajectory,

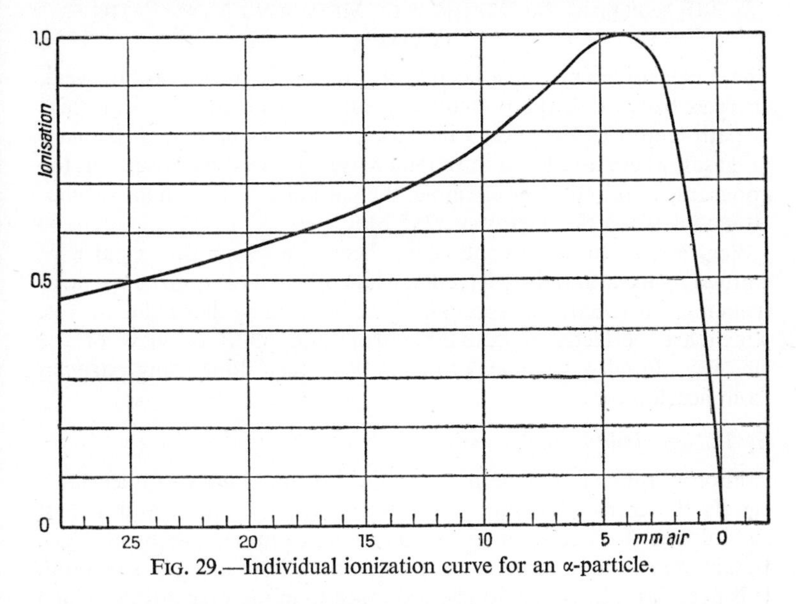

FIG. 29.—Individual ionization curve for an α-particle.

and α for the path fluctuation parameter. The specific ionization along the length of the bundle will be of the order of

$$J(x) = \int_{x}^{\infty} e^{-(\epsilon^2/\alpha^2)}\, i(\epsilon - x)\, d\epsilon,$$

where x is the distance from the point where J is measured to the stopping point of a particle having a path equal to the mean path. It is the path fluctuation which causes the Bragg curve to differ from the ionization curve of an individual particle, and because the parameter α is a function of the energy of the particles the Bragg curves corresponding to the different energies are not superimposable. If the function $i(r)$ is known, the preceding integral will enable us to trace the Bragg curve for different values of α and also to establish the relation between the extrapolated path and the mean path. In this way, for α-particles in air, Holloway and Livingston have established the relation

$$P_{extr} - P_{mean} = 0\cdot 47\alpha - 0\cdot 06,$$

the paths being expressed in mm. of air at 15°C and 760 mm. of Hg. For the α-particles of polonium, for example, for which the mean path is 38·42 mm., the difference is only 0·23 mm., and thus clearly less than 1 per cent.

(4) Experimental Methods of Measuring Mean Paths in Gases

These measurements have been performed only in the case of weak energies because of the difficulties resulting from the rapid increase in path length as the energy increases. This means that in the case of gases, there is also a rapid increase in the dimensions of the apparatus required. For example, the path of a proton in air reaches 10 metres when the energy is 32·5 Mev.

Very many measurements have been made on the α-particles emitted by natural radio-elements, while others have utilized particles from nuclear reactions, especially those induced by thermal neutrons, which are perfectly reproducible from the point of view of the energies. Finally, some experiments have been done using particles from accelerators.

(i) *Wilson cloud chamber method*

Photographs of particle paths in the Wilson cloud chamber show clearly the concept of trajectory and path fluctuations, and at first sight appear to lend themselves admirably to measurement of these. In fact, many measurements have been carried out using this method. It is necessary, however, to pay attention to many precautions which have to be taken in order to arrive at satisfactory results. There are three types of difficulty to be faced if the measured path values are to be valuable:

(*a*) The condensation of droplets on the ions in the cloud chamber results at the moment when the expansion has attained such a value that the vapour within the chamber has reached supersaturation. But the ions may have been formed just before the expansion, or during the expansion, so that there is a certain degree of doubt as to when the trajectories were produced and the exact pressure of the atmosphere in the chamber at that moment, this pressure being that corresponding to the trajectory observed.

(*b*) The atmosphere in the cloud chamber is always a complex one and contains at least two constituents: a gas and a vapour. Since it is simply a question of making comparative measurements in the chamber, one can introduce into the chamber α-particles of a certain energy, for the purpose of calibrating the chamber. If, however, absolute measurements have to be made, these can only be valid for the complex atmosphere of the chamber, and cannot be translated in terms of simpler atmospheres except by rather careful corrections.

(*c*) It sometimes happens that the mounting of the radioactive sample becomes coated with a thin liquid film which causes a slowing down of the particles and thus decreases the path. Thus one must give great attention to the purity of the sources within the chamber.

Provided all the necessary precautions are taken, reliable measurements are possible, and very satisfactory measurements have been made, especially by Irène Curie, and by Blackett and Lees.

(ii) *Differential ionization chamber method*

This method has been developed between 1930 and 1932 by Rutherford and his pupils, more especially Ward, Lewis and Wynn-Williams. We shall describe the method used at that time, although

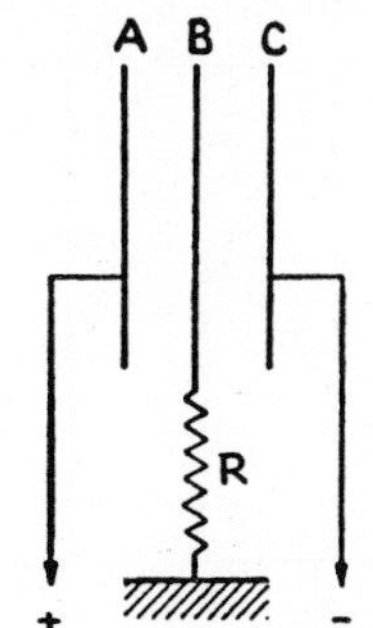

FIG. 30.—Differential ionization chamber for measurement of the mean range of α-particles.

the technical improvements made since then have resulted in appreciable modifications. The apparatus used consists of two ionization chambers with plane parallel electrodes, and one common electrode (Fig. 30). The electrodes A and B are formed from extremely thin metal foils (gold foil of equivalent thickness 0·4 mm. of air). The α-particles, emitted by a natural source and collimated by means of convenient diaphragms, strike normally the electrodes and can produce ions in both of the chambers. The central electrode forms the collector; of the two electrodes A and C, one is at a positive potential, the other at a negative potential to the collecting electrode, so that the latter collects the negative ions formed in the first chamber and the positive ions formed in the second chamber. Thus, the ionization measured for each particle is the difference in the ionizations produced in the two chambers. The depth of each chamber is 2·5 mm.

To each α-particle corresponds, therefore, an impulse of potential upon the collecting electrode proportional to the difference of the ionizations produced in the two chambers by the particle. This impulse is amplified by the amplifier (of the linear type) and finally fed into an oscillograph and registered upon a photographic film.

For each particle passing the entry face of the chamber, then, it is possible to find the potential difference which it creates in the two chambers. What will be the relationship between such an impulse and the point at which the particle is stopped? The curve shown in

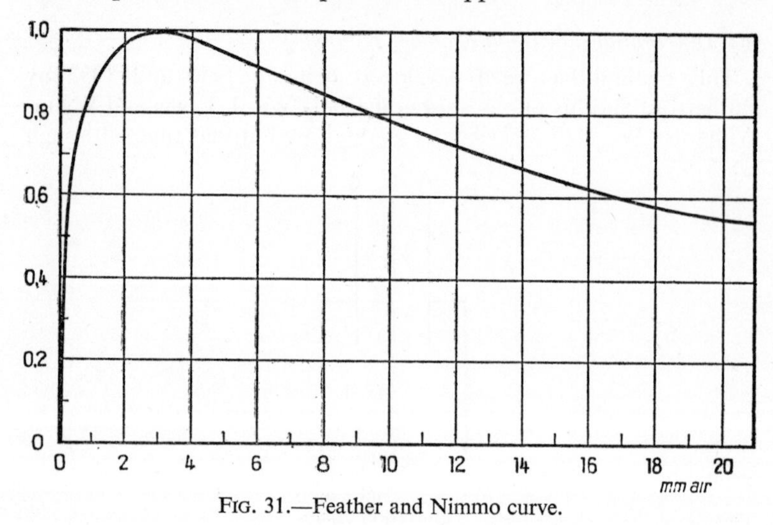

FIG. 31.—Feather and Nimmo curve.

Fig. 31 shows the specific ionization produced by an individual α-particle, deduced from observations made with a cloud chamber by Feather and Nimmo, and used by Rutherford and his collaborators. We shall see later that this curve is inaccurate in some respects, and would nowadays be replaced by the curve deduced from the experiments of Holloway and Livingston (Fig. 29) to be mentioned later. This curve shows a maximum about 3 mm. before the end of the path.

Now let us see how the ionization left by a single α-particle in one of the two chambers varies with respect to the abscissa of its stopping point, measured relative to the entry face of the first chamber. We shall assume the wall thickness negligible, to a first approximation. The ionization is proportional to the area enclosed by the specific ionization curve and the two parallels 2·5 mm. apart, and this variation has the tendency shown by the curve A in Fig. 32. Under the same conditions the ionization left in the rear chamber is shown by the curve B in the same figure and the resultant impulse is obtained as a function of the abscissa of the point of arrest of the α-particle and the difference between the ordinates of the two curves, as shown by curve C. It will be seen how the amplitude passes through a maximum when the α-particle suffers arrest 3 mm. behind the entry face, and that it reaches zero and then changes sign when the point of stopping is 6 mm. behind the entry face.

If we consider only the α-particles giving rise to impulses the amplitude of which is between 70 and 100 per cent of the maximum, we shall be certain that these will be stopped within a distance band 2 mm. wide between 2 and 4 mm. behind the entry face. In the

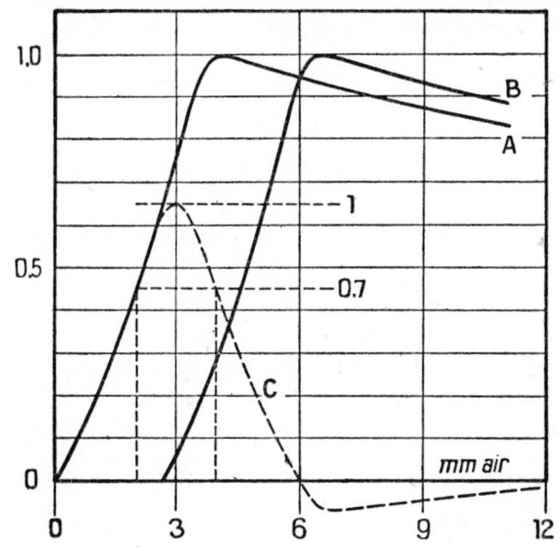

FIG. 32.—Resultant ionization in a differential chamber.

experiments of Rutherford and his co-workers the ionization chambers were placed perpendicularly to a collimated beam of α-particles along the track of the beam and it was noted for various distances between the source and the face of entry of the chamber how many particles were recorded in unit time, with an amplitude between 70 and 100 per cent of the observed maximum. This amounted to noting the number of particles which were stopped within a layer 2 mm. deep and placed 2 mm. behind the entry face, as a function of the position of this layer along the track of the particles. Fig. 33 shows the gaussian law of the fluctuation of the path around the mean path length. The number of particles stopped within a layer 2 mm. thick is proportional to the area cut off by the curve between the two parallels which are 2 mm. apart and is a function also of the position of the middle plane of that layer, as shown by the curve B in the same figure. It is seen to be a bell-shaped curve with the same axis of symmetry, but more spread out than the initial curve. The results of the Rutherford group lead to similar curves when the differential chamber is displaced along the path of the collimated beam of α-particles, and the maximum on the bell-shaped curve is obtained when the mean position of the 2 mm. thick layer is at a distance from the source equal to the mean path of the α-particles from that source.

The various paths of the α-particles from natural radio-elements have been determined in this way, but it should be noted that the specific ionization curve for an individual α-particle as used by Rutherford is nowadays considered to be inaccurate. This means that the position of the mean plane of the effective layer in the chamber is erroneously determined, so that the results are thus all inaccurate

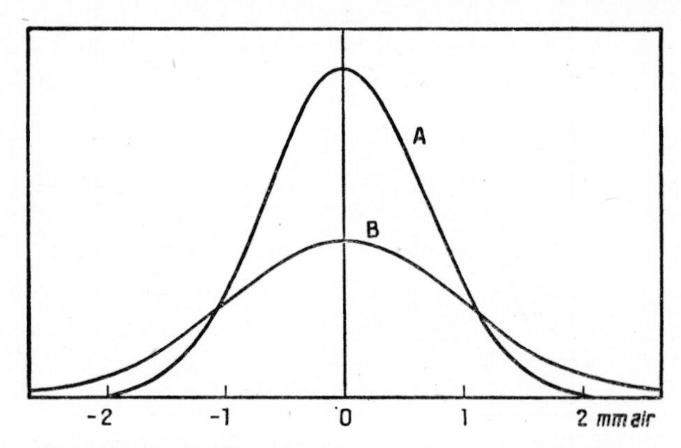

FIG. 33.—Probability of stoppage within a finite thickness.

to a certain extent. A correction, although small, has been deduced by comparison with other methods of measurement, and this will be mentioned later.

(iii) *Counting after ionization*

The experiments now to be described were carried out by Holloway and Livingston in 1938[1], with the object of determining as precisely as possible the range of α-particles from polonium in air.

The ideal experiment for this purpose would be as follows. In the path of a collimated beam of particles from polonium one would place an ionization chamber with parallel electrodes perpendicular to the path of the beam. It would be supposed that the entry face of the chamber is infinitely thin, so that the α-particles would suffer no slowing down, and that the amplifier to which the chamber is connected is sufficiently sensitive to register the potential established between the pair of electrodes by a single α-particle. Under such conditions, each α-particle which passes the entry face of the chamber by any amount, however small, would be recorded, and by moving the chamber along the path of the beam, one would obtain the curve such as that shown in Fig. 28. If N is the maximum number of α-particles recorded per unit time, the mean plane of stopping of the particles will be that which would coincide with the entry face of the chamber when the number of recorded particles becomes $N/2$.

Practical difficulties render such an ideal experiment impossible, and among them are the following. Firstly, one cannot obtain walls which are infinitely thin, and the foils of metal used in the making of the chamber must have finite thickness. Further, there is no amplifier sufficiently sensitive to register the formation of a single pair of ions. All ionization chambers have a background count, and the smallest impulses which can be recorded by such an instrument are of the same order of magnitude as the variations in the background count itself. In the present state of technical development, the finest amplifiers will hardly record with certainty numbers of ion-pairs smaller than 1,000, and at the time of the experiments described, the instruments were even less advanced. Holloway and Livingston conducted their experiments in such a way as to eliminate their inaccuracies by means of a differential method.

They used two ionization chambers the depths of which were 1 mm. and 2 mm., and which we shall refer to as chambers 1 and 2. The entry faces of these chambers were made not from metal foils, but from a metal grid, so that α-particles arriving within the interstices suffered no retardation. As a result, the electric field is not cancelled out in a regular way in the plane of the grid, and the ions formed at a certain distance in front of the grid can be collected and will contribute to the impulse produced. Thus, we may envisage an 'electric entry face' for the chamber, not coincident with the mechanical entry face, and situated at some unknown distance in front of the latter.

Further, the linear amplifier was provided with a discriminator, consisting of a thyratron, and this made possible the counting of impulses which, after amplification, exceeded a given value which could be adjusted at will. This predetermined value, V, we call the discriminator voltage. Having now described briefly the set-up of the experiments, let us consider the theory involved.

We start by asking ourselves what impulses will be recorded in chambers 1 and 2 placed in positions A_1 and A_2 (Fig. 34(a)) which are such that their rear planes are both beyond the planes of the mean paths of the particles. When we consider the trend of the specific ionization curve, we see that in the region of the end of the trajectory where our two ionization chambers are placed, the ionization impulse left by an α-particle will be greater the further to the right the particle is stopped. The ionization impulses will then vary in the same sense as the paths of the particles, and since we adjust the discriminator voltage so that we shall record only those α-particles having an ionization greater than a certain value, we register only the portion of the beam formed by the particles which have longer tracks. By varying the discriminator bias, we obtain a curve which gives the number of particles recorded as a function of V, and this has the form shown in Figure 35. When the discriminator bias is such that, of N particles in the beam per unit time, we record only $N/2$, then these $N/2$ particles are the ones which pass the mean plane, and the discriminator voltage V_A corresponding to the count of these $N/2$ particles is proportional to the ionization left in each chamber by an α-particle for which the path is exactly equal to the mean path.

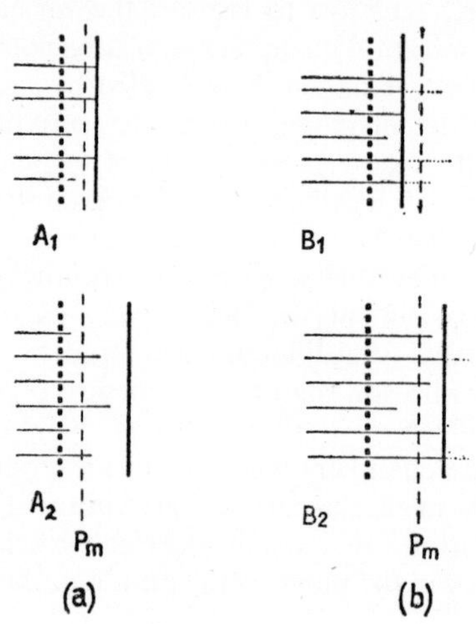

FIG. 34.—Schematic explanation of the experiment of Holloway and Livingston.

In the two positions A_1 and A_2, if we apply to the two chambers potential differences proportional to their depths, the electric fields become identical and the electrical entry faces become situated in front of the geometric faces by the same amount. The discriminator voltage corresponding to the count $N/2$ in the two chambers is thus the same.

Now consider the two chambers in positions B_1 and B_2 (Fig. 34(*b*)) characterized by the fact that the rear plane of chamber 1 is in front of the mean path of the α-particles, while the rear plane of chamber 2 is behind this plane of mean path. The same kind of reasoning will show us that in chamber 2 where conditions are identical to those in position A_2, the discriminator voltage V_{B_2} which reduces the count to $N/2$ is then proportional to the ionization left in the chamber by a particle for which the path equals the mean path.

As far as chamber 1 is concerned, the same conclusion is valid, but an α-particle with a path equal to the mean path no longer becomes stopped in the chamber, and the discriminator voltage V_{B_1} (which is lower than V_{B_2}) corresponding to the count $N/2$ is proportional to the ionization left in the chamber by the α-particle with path equal to the mean path.

If we now trace for various positions of the chambers 1 and 2 the graphs of the discriminator voltages corresponding to the half-count as a function of the distance between the entrance grill and the source, the result appears as shown in Fig. 36, where, as one can see, in region I the curves are merged, but in region II they separate. On the basis of analysis, the point of divergence of the two curves corresponds to a position of the chamber such that the rear face of

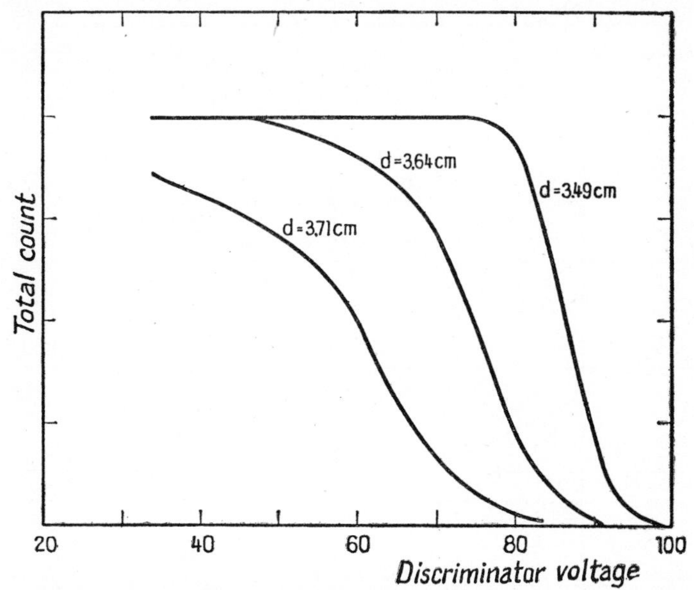

FIG. 35.—Number of α-particles counted as a function of the discriminator bias for different positions of chamber 1.

chamber 1 is exactly at a distance from the source equal to the mean path of the particles used. In the work of Holloway and Livingston this separation is obtained with an abscissa for the grill entrance equal to 37·06 mm., and as the actual depth of the chamber was 0·92 mm., the mean path was 37·98 mm. After the application of corrections for temperature and pressure of air, the mean path of the α-particles from polonium (5·303 Mev) is found to be $38 \cdot 40 \pm 0 \cdot 1$ mm. in air at 15°C and 760 mm. pressure.

Consider now the curve III, which represents the difference between the ordinates of the curves I and II. The ordinates, as we have seen, will represent the ionization left by an α-particle arrested upon the plane of the mean path, between a stopping point a and the point $a+0 \cdot 92$. If we now consider a point b as ordinate, within the section which is common to the two curves I and II, then this ordinate will be a measure of the ionization left in the chamber by an α-particle being arrested on a plane of mean path lying between this plane and the abscissa $b-\epsilon$, where ϵ is the difference (or distance) between the electrical entry face and the mechanical entry face of the chamber. Clearly, the two curves can be interconverted by moving them through an amplitude equal to $0 \cdot 92+\epsilon$. The experimental work has shown that ϵ was, for the conditions in question, equal to $0 \cdot 39$ mm.

Obviously, if curve III is lowered to the extent of $1 \cdot 31$ mm., then curves I and II will pass through the point where their ordinate is zero (Fig. 36).

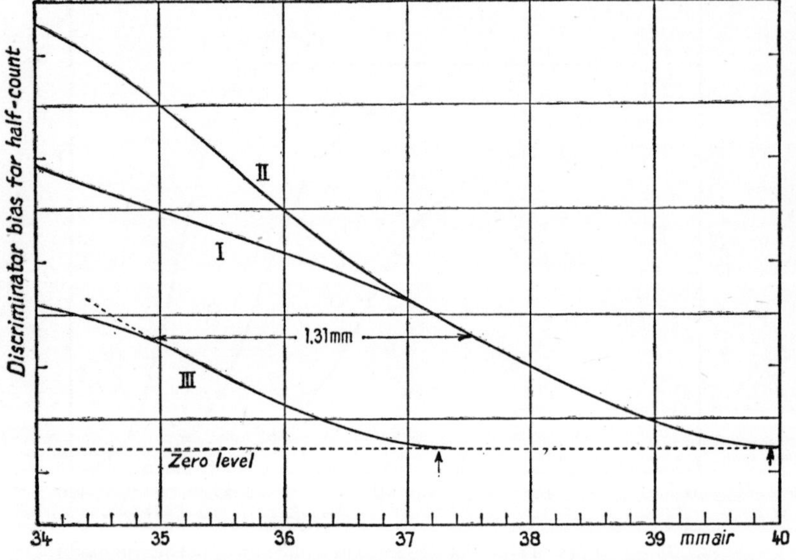

FIG. 36.—Variation of discriminator bias for half-count as function of distance.

Curve II when thus completed represents the ionization left by a particle within the last few mm. of its path, and by differentiation of this function we may deduce the specific ionization of a single α-particle. For distances greater than a few mm. from the end of the track, the specific ionization of the particle which is stopped on the plane of the mean track has been measured as a function of the distance from the source, taking it as equal to the mean value of the specific ionization left for different particles at the same distance from the source, whatever may be their track. This specific ionization, to a first approximation, may be taken as equal to $\Delta I/\Delta l$, where ΔI is the ionization left in the chamber of depth Δl, the mean plane being at the chosen distance from the source. Such an expression may be corrected to bring it to the value of dI/dl, or the corresponding value for an infinitely small thickness of the chamber, if this is necessary.

From a series of data, Holloway and Livingston have deduced the individual ionization curve of an α-particle, as shown in Figs. 29 and 37.

(iv) *Indirect methods of deduction of mean path from Bragg curves*

We have already shown that the ordinate of the Bragg curve for a point distant x from the mean path is given by

$$J = \int_{x}^{\infty} e^{-\epsilon^2/\alpha^2} i(\epsilon - x)\, d\epsilon.$$

For practical purposes, rather than use this formula, which is based on an analytical form for the function i, it is preferable to make a numerical calculation on the integral. This was done by Holloway and Livingston for different values of α, making use of the function i that is represented in Fig. 37, which holds for air. The result is that between the path extrapolated from the Bragg method and the mean path, there exists the relationship

$$P_{extr} - P_{mean} = 0 \cdot 47\alpha - 0 \cdot 06 \quad \text{in mm. units.}$$

If now we can deduce α from a Bragg curve, the relation given will enable us to calculate the correction necessary for application to the extrapolated path in order to obtain the mean path. Now α is not directly measurable from the Bragg curves, but the construction carried out by Holloway and Livingston makes it possible to construct the tangent to the point of inflection of the Bragg curve, and the difference y of the abscissæ of this point of intersection with the axis of abscissæ on the one hand and with the tangent at the maximum (the ordinate being conventionally taken as equal to unity) on the other hand, is linked with α by the relationship

$$\alpha = 0 \cdot 917y - 1 \cdot 60 \text{ mm.}$$

Here y is conveniently measured from the experimental curves, and so one obtains α and $P_{extr} - P_{mean}$.

This has been done by Holloway and Livingston, making use of the Bragg curves of various workers, and the table below shows some of the results obtained:

Worker	Source of particle	Extrapolated path	y	α	$P_{extr} - P_{mean}$	P_{mean}	Cambridge
Henderson	ThC′	86·16±0·04	3·04	1·19	0·50	85·66±0·07	85·70
Henderson	RaC′	69·53±0·04	2·92	1·08	0·45	69·08±0·06	69·07
I. Curie	Po	38·70±0·06	2·42	0·62	0·23	38·47±0·07	38·42 (for the three Po values)
						38·45±0·06	
Naidu	Po	38·68±0·06	2·46	0·66	0·25	38·43±0·07	

The final column in the foregoing table shows the results of measurements made by the Cambridge group using the differential chamber method, with a correction of 0·37 mm. on the original figures, this correction being to compensate the error derived from the use of an erroneous specific ionization curve for the particle, the

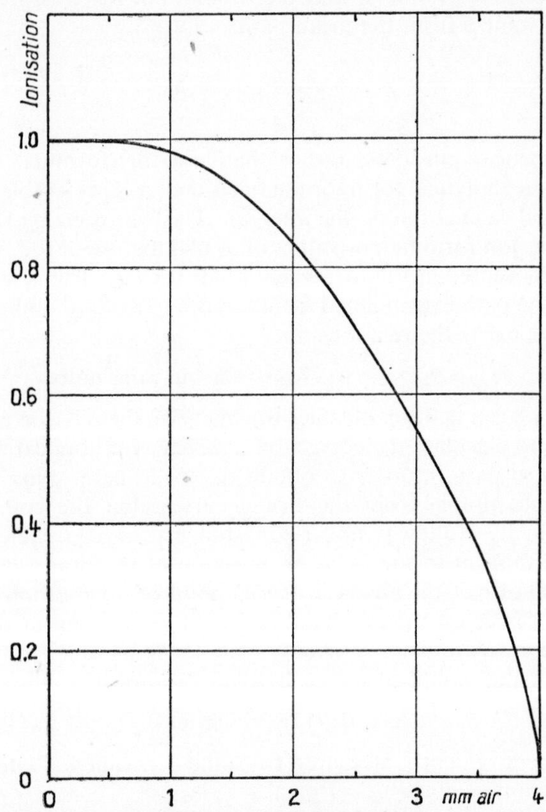

FIG. 37.—Final portion of ionization-distance curve for an individual α-particle.

correction having been chosen in order to give best agreement with values obtained by other methods. In the particular case of polonium, if we take together all the results obtained as shown, it will be seen that the mean value for the path of the α-particles from this source may be assumed equal to $38 \cdot 42 \pm 0 \cdot 06$ mm., under normal conditions.

(v) *Results for protons and α-particles in air*

The following table, due to Jesse and Sadauskis[2], gives the relation between energy and path for protons and α-particles in air at 15°C and 760 mm. pressure, for tracks smaller than 5 cm.

Mean path in cm.	Energy of particles in Mev	Energy of protons in Mev	Mean path in cm.	Energy of particles in Mev	Energy of protons in Mev
0·20	0·271		2·30	3·785	1·002
0·25	0·382		2·40	3·806	1·027
0·30	0·508		2·50	4·003	1·051
0·35	0·635		2·60	4·103	1·077
0·40	0·761	0·302	2·70	4·200	1·103
0·45	0·882		2·80	4·300	1·128
0·50	0·994	0·357	2·90	4·400	1·154
0·55	1·105		3·00	4·502	1·179
0·60	1·214	0·106	3·10	4·602	1·202
0·65	1·320		3·20	4·702	1·226
0·70	1·422	0·453	3·30	4·798	1·250
0·75	1·525		3·40	4·891	1·274
0·80	1·624	0·499	3·50	4·987	1·296
0·85	1·723		3·60	5·079	1·318
0·90	1·816	0·541	3·70	5·169	1·340
0·95	1·908		3·80	5·260	1·362
1·00	1·995	0·581	3·90	5·350	1·384
1·10	2·162	0·619	4·00	5·440	1·406
1·20	2·321	0·656	4·10	5·527	1·428
1·30	2·470	0·692	4·20	5·614	1·450
1·40	2·620	0·728	4·30	5·698	1·471
1·50	2·767	0·764	4·40	5·783	1·492
1·60	2·907	0·796	4·50	5·870	1·513
1·70	3·044	0·827	4·60	5·953	1·534
1·80	3·174	0·859	4·70	6·035	1·554
1·90	3·306	0·889	4·80	6·120	1·574
2·00	3·425	0·919	4·90	6·202	1·594
2·10	3·549	0·948	5·00	6·281	1·614
2·20	3·668	0·977			

(5) Experimental Measurement of Track in a Solid Medium

The principle of this type of measurement is a logical consequence of the definition of mean path. A source, such as a radio-element or an accelerator, supplies a collimated beam of particles of fixed energy, travelling *in vacuo*. At a certain distance is placed a detector, which might be a scintillation apparatus, G.M. tube, ionization chamber, etc., and between the two is placed a certain thickness (which can be increased as required) of the solid material to be studied, and one measures the number of particles passing the metal foil, as a function of the thickness of the foil. From the results is drawn a graph, such as that in Fig. 28, and the mean path is then obtained from the thickness which reduces the intensity of the beam by half.

The difficulty attending such measurements is the same as that in the measurements performed on gases. The method necessitates having a detector which will record a particle leaving the metal foil and at such an energy that it cannot even produce one more pair of ions. In most cases, of course, the experiment is carried out in such a way that the path is not completed within the metal foil, and the foil thickness measured is then somewhat smaller than the mean path. All the particles emerge from the foil, and then one can trace the Bragg curve for them in their passage through a gas. Then follows an analysis similar to that already described for gaseous media, so that the residual track in the gas is determined, and this, when translated in terms of the solid medium used, is a correction to be applied to the mean path recorded for the metal foil.

Various workers[3] have carried out experiments with various media and with particles of energies up to 340 Mev.

In spite of the numerous experiments which have been performed, there still has not been obtained with the required degree of certainty the relationship between energy and path for particles of very low energies, i.e. below 1 Mev in the case of protons, and 4 Mev in the case of α-particles. Since calculations are by no means easy in the case of solid media, it would be highly desirable that more information should be available.

The table given below, due to Bethe and Ashkin[4], gives some results for the tracks of protons in aluminium, copper and lead. These are essentially calculated values, but the values experimentally determined confirm them generally to within 1–2 per cent. We may conclude that the range, expressed in terms of mass per unit area, is greater in the case of media of greater atomic weight.

Energy (Mev)	Al	Cu		Pb	
1	3·3 mg.cm^{-2}	4·5 mg.cm^{-2}	(0·74)	8·1 mg.cm^{-2}	(0·41)
2	10·8	14·5	(0·745)	25·5	(0·42)
3	21·2	28·5	(0·745)	49·0	(0·43)
4	34·0	45·5	(0·75)	78·0	(0·44)
5	50·5	66·0	(0·765)	113·0	(0·45)
6	69·0	90·0	(0·765)	152·0	(0·46)
7	89·0	166·0	(0·765)	193·0	(0·46)
8	113·0	145·0	(0·780)	240·0	(0·47)
9	138·0	175·0	(0·79)	290·0	(0·48)
10	167·0	210·0	(0·795)	345·0	(0·49)
20	565·0	700·0	(0·81)	1·09 g.cm^{-2}	(0·52)
50	2·85 g.cm^{-2}	3·5 g.cm^{-2}	(0·815)	5·0	(0·57)
100	9·80	11·5	(0·85)	16·7	(0·59)
500	145·0	168·0	(0·865)	230·0	(0·63)
1000	405·0	475·0	(0·85)	620·0	(0·65)

Figs. 38 and 39 represent the relation between energy and range for α-particles in air, the Figures being due to Rosenblum and Wilcox, and the metal being gold.

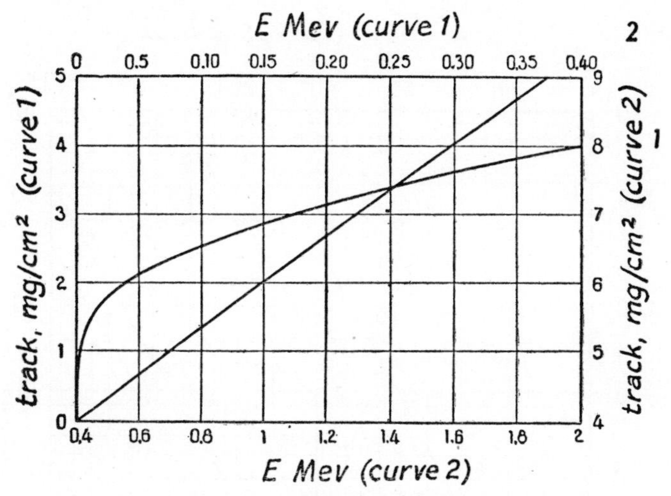

FIG. 38.—Energy-track relationship for α-particles in gold.

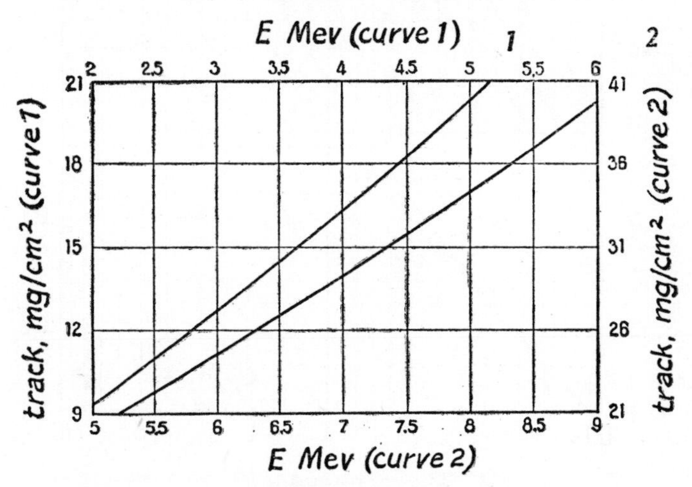

FIG. 39.—Energy-track relationship for α-particles in gold.

An especially important solid medium, and one which is involved in some very important techniques, is the photographic emulsion. In such a medium, the ionizing particles affect the plate provided sufficient ion-pairs are produced. When the film is developed, the track appears as a line of grains, and the distance between the first and last of these represents the length of the trajectory. Different types of commercial emulsions differ in composition, and the relationship between energy and range is valid only for a given emulsion.

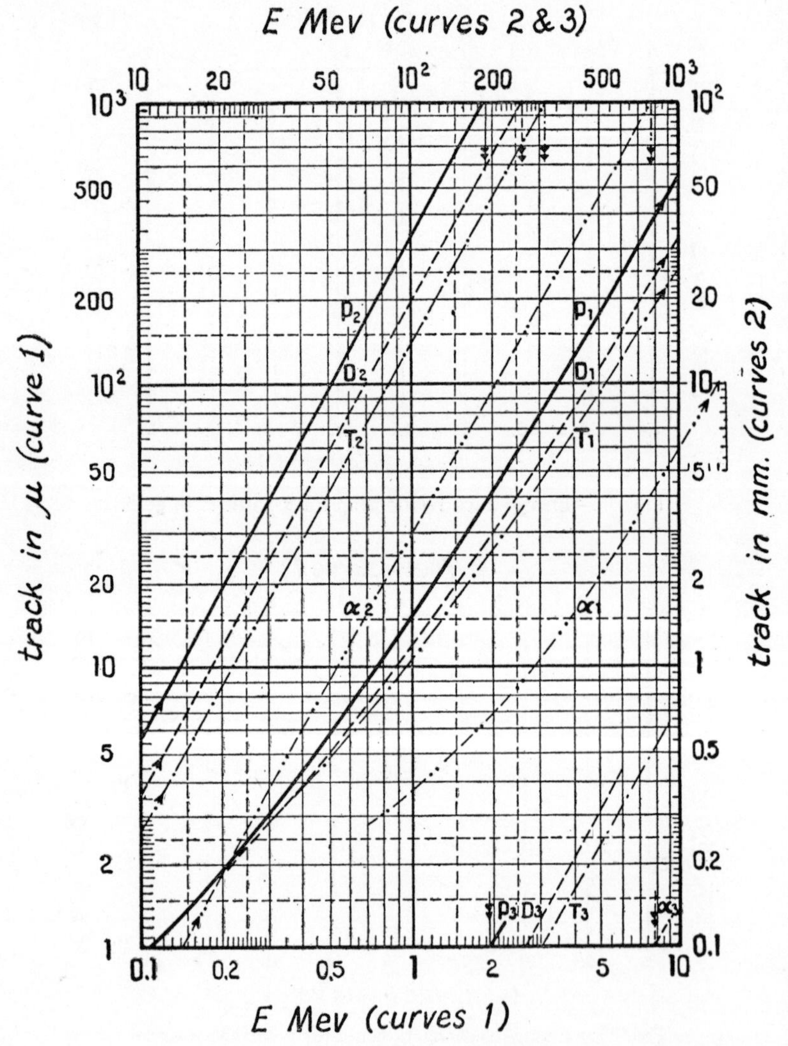

FIG. 40.—Energy-track relationships of protons in C_2 emulsions.

As an example, Fig. 40 gives the energy-range relationship for protons, deuterons, tritons, and α-particles in emulsions C_2 made by Ilford, as deduced by Vigneron[5], agreeing with known experimental values.

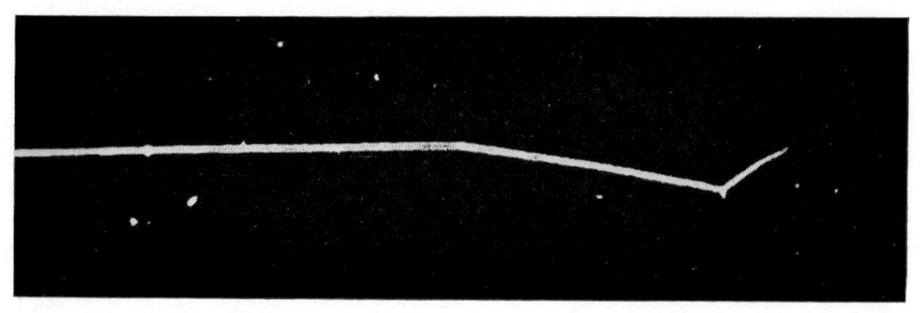

Fig. 41.—Coulombic deflections of an α-particle at the end of its track in air; the length of the trajectory shown is the last 12 mm. of its track in normal air.

(6) Stopping Power

Just as we have already defined the power of a medium for slowing down particles, by the expression $R = -\mathrm{d}T/\mathrm{d}x$, we can also define the stopping power of a medium for any particle by the quotient T/P, or the kinetic energy of the particle divided by the range necessary for complete loss of that energy. Like the decelerating power, this must also be a function of the energy T.

Likewise, we can define the relative stopping power of substance 1 compared with that for substance 2 for an equally energized particle by the reciprocal ratio of the ranges. In the table on p. 82, are shown in brackets the relative stopping powers for copper and lead compared with aluminium for various energies. It will be seen (and this is a general law) that this relative stopping power is a slowly increasing function of energy for the heavier elements, while in the case of the lighter elements, it is a slowly decreasing function.

REFERENCES

1. Holloway, M. G., and Livingston, M. S. (1938), *Phys. Rev.*, **54,** 18.
2. Jesse, W. P., and Sadauskis, J. (1950), *Phys. Rev.*, **78,** 1.
3. Mather, L. R., and Segre, E. (1951), *Phys. Rev.*, **84,** 191.
4. Segré, E., *Experimental Nuclear Physics*, Vol. 1, Part 2.
5. Vigneron, L. (1953), *Journal de Physique*, **14,** 145.

Chapter 8

COULOMBIC INTERACTION OF LIGHT ATOMIC PARTICLES WITH NUCLEI

(1) General

We have discussed the fact that light atomic particles undergo essentially simple interactions with the electrons of matter, but it sometimes happens that they approach sufficiently near to an atomic nucleus to suffer interaction with this. If the impact parameter is great, then the law of force is the coulombic law which involves the charges on the incident particle and on the target nucleus, and this law may be applied to the impacts mentioned in Chapter 2, provided the coulombic law holds. The same applies when the impact parameter is small but the kinetic energy of the incident particle insufficient to cause it to make a near approach to the nucleus, i.e., when the energy is so small that the minimum distance of approach, $b = Zze^2/T$, remains relatively large. This type of nuclear interaction, in which the coulombic law can be applied, may be termed the 'exceptional' type, to indicate that the rarity of occurrence is very marked by contrast with those interactions which cause ionization or excitation.

Sometimes it happens that the impact parameter and the minimum distance of approach are comparatively small, so that the incident particle approaches the nucleus sufficiently to ensure that the specific nuclear forces come into play. By nuclear forces we mean those forces, still very imperfectly understood, acting between the nucleons, and keeping them together in the nucleus. These forces are characterized by a small radius of action, of the order of 10^{-13} cm., and when two nuclei approach in such a way that their distance apart is reduced to this order of dimensions, the specific nuclear forces come into play. The coulombic law then no longer applies, and is insufficient to explain the phenomena of the impact, and in particular, the Rutherford formula can no longer be applied.

The study of nuclear reactions is of considerable importance since it forms one of the chief methods of understanding nuclear forces, and in recent years it has been the subject of much experimentation. To push considerations to the limit, when the kinetic energy is sufficiently large, so that the incident particle can penetrate the nucleus, it may produce there the phenomena which we call nuclear reactions or transmutations.

The study of interactions and nuclear reactions, although of great theoretical and practical importance, is rather out of the sphere of this book, and because of the rarity of their occurrence in the slowing down of atomic particles, these questions will not be further studied here. We shall, in fact, limit our considerations to cases in which the coulombic law can be applied.

(2) Coulombic Interactions of Light Atomic Particles with Nuclei

When there is interaction between particles of about the same mass, it is to be expected that the deflection and the interchange of energy will be comparatively important.

As far as deflection is concerned, this is governed, for energies which are not of the relativistic order, at least, by the Rutherford formula (formula 15, Chapter 2) which gives the effective differential section of diffusion in the element of solid angle $d\Omega$ within the angle ϕ,

$$d\sigma_{\Omega} = \frac{Z^2 z^2 e^4}{M^2 V^4} \frac{\left[\cos\phi \pm \sqrt{\left(1 - \frac{M^2}{m^2}\sin^2\phi\right)}\right]^2}{\sin^4\phi \sqrt{\left(1 - \frac{M^2}{m^2}\sin^2\phi\right)}}.$$

This formula indicates that the effective section is inversely proportional to V^4, and as a result, the deflections become more and more frequent as the particle becomes decelerated. This is a characteristic which is made very obvious in the trajectory photographs for α-particles taken by means of the Wilson cloud chamber technique, where the deflections during nuclear impacts are seen especially towards the ends of the tracks (Fig. 41).

If the study of coulombic interaction of light atomic particles and nuclei is nowadays approaching the state of being abandoned, interest is well maintained in regions where nuclear forces come into play. The part which the former played in the historical development of the subject must not be underestimated, however. The study consists in observing the angular distribution of α-particles after deflection through thin metal foils, and this method led Rutherford to notice that this distribution was what one would expect if each atom consisted of a relatively heavy electrically-charged central body which repelled the α-particles. Thus, in 1913, he was able to prove experimentally the existence of atomic nuclei, agreeing with the suggestion made earlier by Jean Perrin.

Towards 1930, many studies had been made by Rutherford and his school, always making use of α-particles as the projectiles. It is these principles which we now need to discuss.* They have given support to the Rutherford formula, and form a verification of the coulombic law in the vicinity of the nucleus, and also show that the charge number and the atomic number are identical.

* There is a much more detailed account in *Radiations from Radioactive Substances*, Rutherford, Chadwick and Ellis (Cambridge, 1930), new edit. 1951.

The first experiments of a systematic nature (1913) were due to Geiger and Marsden, who studied the deflection of α-particles in their passage through foils of silver and gold. For heavy substances we can neglect the term $(M/m\sin\phi)^2$ in comparison with unity, and then rewrite the Rutherford formula in a simplified form, as

$$d\sigma_\Omega = \frac{Z^2z^2e^4}{M^2V^4}\cdot\frac{(1+\cos\phi)^2}{\sin^4\phi}\cdot d\Omega$$

$$d\sigma_\Omega = \frac{Z^2z^2e^4}{4M^2V^4}\cdot\frac{1}{\sin^4\phi/2}\cdot d\Omega.$$

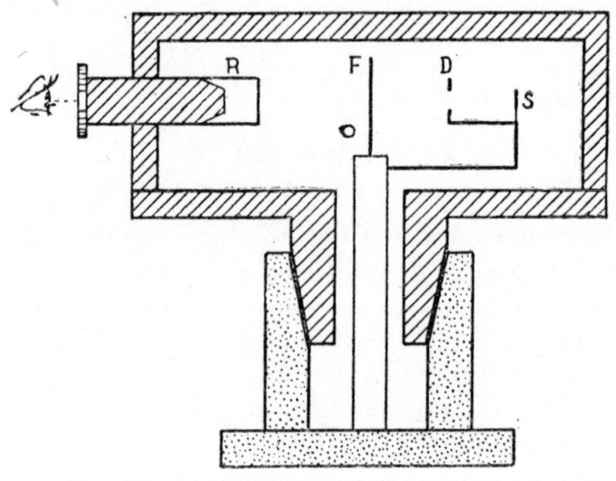

FIG. 42.—Apparatus used by Geiger and Marsden for verifying the Rutherford formula.

The experimental arrangement is shown in Fig. 42, in which S is the source of α-particles (a thin tube of radon), D a diaphragm to limit the beam, F the metal diffusing foil containing n nuclei per sq. cm., R the receiver with a ZnS screen, upon which one observes the scintillations by means of a microscope, each scintillation indicating the arrival of an α-particle diffused through an angle ϕ. The arrangement SDF is fixed, while R can be rotated around the point of impact of the beam upon F, the distance r being kept constant. If dS is the surface area of the screen, then $d\Omega = dS/r^2$, and the fraction f of the particles striking R is equal to

$$f = \frac{Z^2z^2e^4}{4M^2V^4}n\frac{dS}{r^2}\cdot\frac{1}{\sin^4\phi/2}\cdot$$

In counting the number of scintillations $N(\phi)$ for various angles, the counts being constant within experimental limits, Geiger and Marsden showed that, in the case of the particular elements studied, the product $N(\phi)\sin^4(\phi/2)$ remained constant as ϕ varied between 5 and 150° (i.e. as the value of $\sin^4\phi/2$ varied between limits which were in a ratio of 1:250,000. The same workers have also proved that, within the range 6·3 to 2 Mev, the fraction of particles diffused by the foil was proportional to V^{-4}.

Chadwick later confirmed this in the case of platinum.

(3) Measuring the Nuclear Charge

The Rutherford formula enables us to determine the nuclear charge *Ze*. The first efforts in this direction were made by Geiger and Marsden, but these led only to some indication of the order of values. The measurements were again undertaken by Chadwick in 1920, when he worked with copper, silver and platinum.

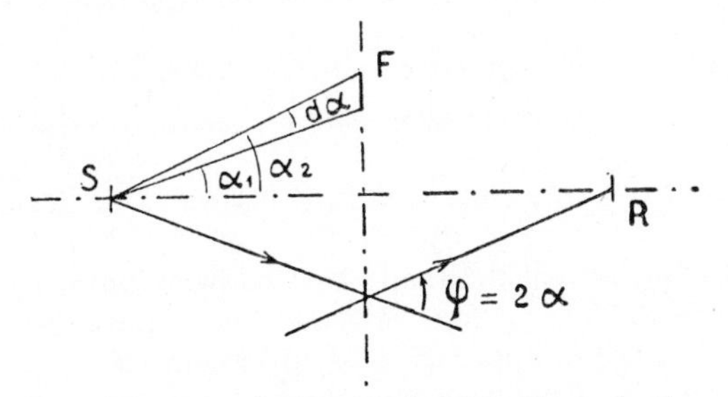

Fig. 43.—Set-up used by Chadwick for determination of nuclear charge.

The experimental arrangement is shown in Fig. 43, and was different from that used by Geiger and Marsden, since in order to increase the intensity of the diffused beam, the diffusing foil F was in the form of a ring, its axis being SR, and its position equidistant from R and S. Calculation shows that the number of rays received upon the surface dS of R is given by the following expression:

$$q = Q\frac{Z^2z^2e^4}{2M^2V^4}\cdot n\cdot\frac{dS}{(SR)^2}\cdot\int_{\alpha_1}^{\alpha_2}\frac{\cos^2\alpha}{\sin^3\alpha}\cdot d\alpha.$$

Here Q represents the total number of particles emitted by the point source.

The determination of Z now means measuring q, ϕ, the geometrical characteristics of the apparatus, and the speed V of the α-particles used, n being the number of nuclei per sq. cm. of the screen used. With the α-particles from RaC, Chadwick found

Cu: $Z = 29\cdot3$ Ag: $Z = 46\cdot3$ Pt: $Z = 77\cdot4$

with an estimated accuracy of 1–2 per cent. The values of the atomic number being respectively 29, 47, and 78, these values confirm in a very direct way the knowledge already gained by means of spectroscopy.

(4) Nuclear Dimensions

The agreement observed between theoretical formula and the results of experimental determinations gives us confidence in the applicability of the coulombic law in the whole province around the diffusing nucleus in which the particle has been moving. In fact, these experiments do not provide a completely accurate confirmation, but indicate the degree of agreement between theoretical forecasts and the values measured from the optical spectra of atoms, the values being based on the use of the coulombic law.

The smallest distance of approach of the α-particle to the nucleus is given by

$$d = \frac{Zze^2}{V^2}\left(\frac{1}{m}+\frac{1}{M}\right)\left(1+\frac{1}{\cos\theta}\right).$$

In an apparatus such as that used by Chadwick, the deviation angle ϕ being known, one can deduce the value of θ, and hence that of d. In the measurements made by Chadwick with platinum, the α-particles with the highest velocities were those which had a minimum distance of approach of 7×10^{-12} cm.

Rutherford and Chadwick have carried out systematic measurements on gold, platinum, silver and copper, using α-particles with ranges of 2·4 to 6·7 cm. in air. They were unable to show any divergences among their experimental results as compared with forecast results based on coulombic law, as regards the fraction of particles diffused and also the variation of this with the energy of the particles. The maximum distances of approach were from $3{\cdot}2\times10^{-12}$ cm. in the case of gold, 2×10^{-12} cm. for silver, and $1{\cdot}2\times10^{-12}$ cm. for copper. The validity of the coulombic law indicates that the nucleus has a radius smaller than these values.

In the case of natural α-particles, the energies are insufficient to allow satisfactory approach to the nuclei in question. In order to achieve smaller approach distances we must either make use of the artificial α-particles from nuclear reactions, or study diffusing nuclei of lighter elements, which have a feebler coulombic repulsion.

Deflection of α-particles by magnesium and aluminium has been studied by Bieler and by Rutherford and Chadwick, and there have been demonstrated effects differing from those expected from theory. Fig. 45 shows Bieler's results, and in the graph the ordinates are for R values, where R is the ratio between the observed deflection of the particle and that calculated for the α-particles from Po and Ra (B+C).

FIG. 44.—Impact of an α-particle with an atomic nucleus in a gas in a Wilson chamber; the α-particle is deflected, and the nucleus projected (in this case, a helium nucleus) forwards. Because both particles are of equal mass, the angle at the fork is 90°, although it appears slightly acute, since the observer is not quite normal to the plane of the two tracks.

The deviations in the deflections in the case of the very small values of R indicate a decrease of the repulsive forces forecast by the coulombic law for particles corresponding to those which penetrate closest to the nuclei.

The study of the deflections of α-particles in hydrogen and helium has shown great deviations from theoretical expectations.

One might adopt the simple explanation for such deviations, and say that they are the result of the intervention of specific nuclear forces coming into play in the case of small approach distances, but we run into difficulty when we try to give quantitative explanations. In fact, we then run up against the well-known difficulties inherent in the treatment of the forces between nucleons.

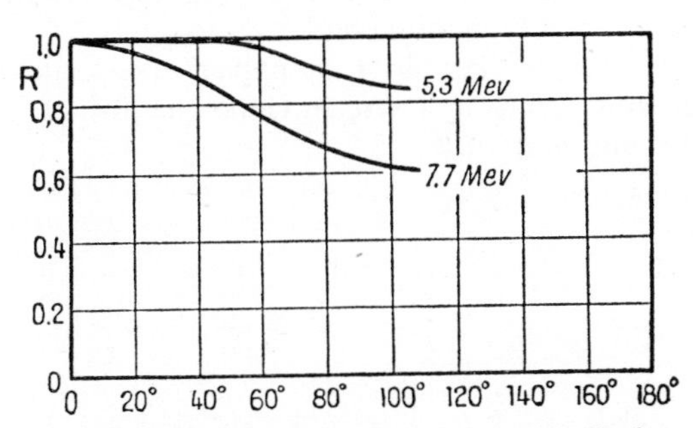

FIG. 45.—Relation (R) between differential effective cross-sections as measured, to those calculated from the Rutherford formula, for the particles in aluminium (after Bieler).

There is a particular phenomenon which occurs during the purely electrostatic deflection of α-particles by helium nuclei. Since the two nuclei involved in this case are identical, it becomes necessary to invoke the principle of uncertainty, for it becomes impossible to distinguish, after the collision, which was originally the moving particle and which the target nucleus. This principle, in fact, has led to the introduction of the idea of exchange forces to supplement the coulombic forces, so that the quantum forces involved modify the phenomena associated with purely electrostatic forces. This effect has been studied by Mott, who has deduced a formula to express the deflection occurring in the case of two identical particles, and the formula has been verified experimentally, and differs markedly from that put forward by Rutherford.

(5) PROJECTED ATOMS

When the energy lost by a moving particle as a result of an impact is large enough, the nucleus receiving the energy can in its turn have a trajectory sufficiently long to become observable.

For example, in the case of the impact between an α-particle and a hydrogen nucleus, the energy transferred to the proton can attain 16/25, or more than half of the energy of the incident particle. As we have already seen, the proton and the α-particle have trajectories of equal length when the energy of the proton is one-quarter that of the other particle, and in such a case the trajectory of the projected particle may even be greater than that of the incident particle. Protons which are projected by impact with other particles are called 'H rays'.

In a more general way, the energy which can be transferred during an impact is greatest when the masses of the two particles lie close together in magnitude, and when light particles are moving within a medium consisting of heavy nuclei the trajectories of the latter are short, and may even be unobservable.

Fig. 44 shows a photograph of the impact of α-particles upon the nuclei of gaseous atoms in a Wilson cloud chamber, and one atom has been put into motion.

Chapter 9

SLOWING DOWN OF FISSION FRAGMENTS

The study of the slowing down of fission fragments with matter is of practical as well as theoretical interest. Upon the phenomenon of fission rest all the methods for production of nuclear energy from uranium or plutonium at the present moment. About 80 per cent of the energy disengaged during a fission appears as kinetic energy of the fission fragments, and so the dissipation of such energy within the medium during the slowing down of these fragments is one of the stages of the transformation of the energy into heat. Further, fission fragments are the only atoms of medium atomic number which we can obtain with relatively high kinetic energy. They may thus be taken as representative of the medium-sized atoms.

(1) General Features of Fission Fragments

A study of the phenomena of fission really falls outside of the province of this book, and we must limit ourselves to a mention of some of the results which must be understood before it is possible to deal adequately with what follows. We shall not deal with the methods by which results were so obtained.

The commonest case of fission is that which occurs when the U-235 atom captures a neutron of thermal energy. This results in the formation of U-236 in a highly excited state, and one of the possible methods of evolution of this nucleus is to disrupt into two pieces of mass of medium mass. At the same time as this fission occurs, two or three new neutrons are liberated, and the phenomenon can be expressed by the following equations:

$$^{236}_{92}\text{U} \rightarrow {}^{A_1}_{Z_1}X + {}^{A_2}_{Z_2}Y + 2 \text{ or } 3 \text{ neutrons}$$

and
$$Z_1 + Z_2 = 92$$

and
$$A_1 + A_2 = 234 \text{ or } 233.$$

The method by which the mass divides is subject to a certain degree of variation, within certain limits, and the probability that the various possible fissions will occur can be calculated for various values of A. The probability is expressed in the curve shown in Fig. 46. It will be seen that the most probable fission route is that corresponding to an asymmetrical fission such that $A_1 = 95$ and $A_2 = 138$, and that the probabilities of other fissions are rapidly becoming smaller when we progress to either side of this value. It will be noted that the symmetrical fission, where $A_1 = A_2 = 117$ is very unlikely.

The asymmetrical nature of this fission process allows us, in the absence of any better method of classification of the fission fragments, to classify these into two groups: the light group, for which the most probable mass is 95, and a heavy group for which the mass

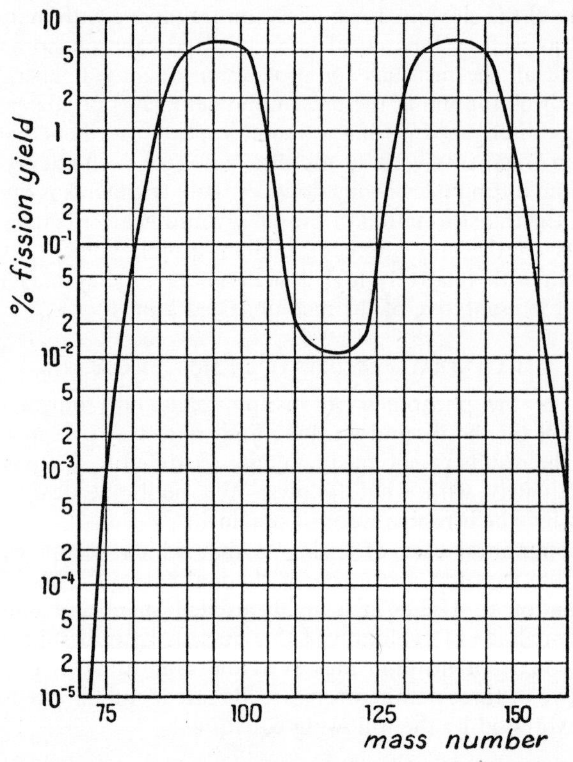

FIG. 46.—Mass probability curve for fission of uranium by thermal neutrons.

of greatest probability is 138. This classification will be used in the following treatment.

Fission is an exoergic phenomenon, and the liberated energy, at the moment of fission, is carried mainly by the two fission fragments in the form of kinetic energy. A small amount is also carried by the liberated neutrons, and some by the γ-rays which are also formed.

Fluctuations in the method of fission naturally involve similar fluctuations in the amount of energy emitted in individual fissions, and hence in the kinetic energy of the fission fragments. The most probable value of the latter is, however, 160 Mev.

The kinetic energy is shared between the two fragments in inverse ratio to their masses, and the probability curves have been determined (Fig. 47). The most probable energy for the heavy particle group is 64 Mev (corresponding to a speed of $0{\cdot}93 \times 10^9$ cm./sec. for a mass of 138), and for the heavy group particles it is 96 Mev (i.e. a speed of $1{\cdot}4 \times 10^9$ cm./sec. for a mass of 95).

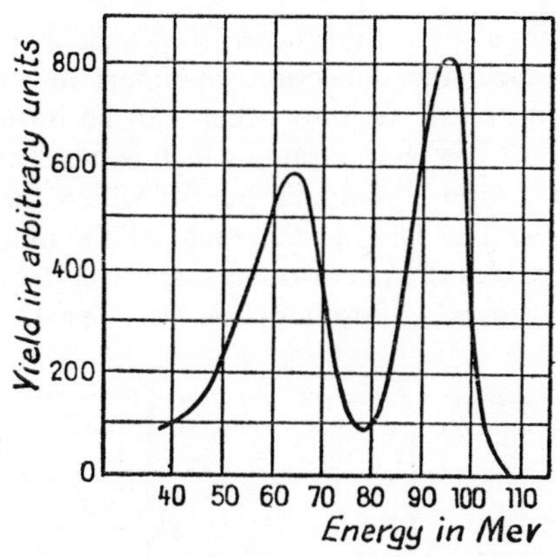

FIG. 47.—Probability curve for kinetic energy of each of the two fission fragments.

(2) CHARGE VARIATION OF FISSION FRAGMENTS

In most measurements of the behaviour of fission fragments, such as were carried out by Lassen[1], the two groups formed by the light and the heavy particles were just considered in this way without any effort to distinguish between the various particles in each group, although it is known that these vary widely in nature, charge, velocity and kinetic energy. Thus the measurements can be but average determinations, and large deviations would be reasonably expected if the individual particles were to come under consideration.

Because of the great number of electrons involved in each atom, there is no possibility of expressing the effective cross-sections for individual processes, and we are limited to measurements of the mean effective charges and the variations of these with the speed of the fragments.

The action of a magnetic field upon the fragments gives a radius of curvature proportional to mv/e_{eff} and we assume the fragments are all emitted with the same velocity, which is equal to the mean value, or mv for the particles is constant (this is true within 10 per cent). The measurement of mv then gives us a method of finding v_{eff}.

The principle of the apparatus as used by Lassen is shown in Fig. 48. The source of the fission fragments is a thin strip of uranium, R, submitted to neutron bombardment. We select a fraction of the fission particles having a radius of curvature of path determined by the position of the slit F′, which is movable, and this, taken in conjunction with the position of the source R and the fixed slit F″, gives the path of the fragments which pass through the collimation system. The apparatus is so calibrated that we know, for a given magnetic field, the relation between the position of the movable slit and the radius of curvature.

The slit F″ is closed by a thin metal foil which separates the first part of the enclosure (the deflection chamber) in which one can produce a vacuum at will, or into which can be introduced a gas, from the second part of the apparatus which is filled with gas and is fitted with an ionization chamber inside of which the fission fragments lose their energy. The measurement of the amplitude of the current impulse enables the operator to know whether the fragment belongs to the light particle family or the heavy part.

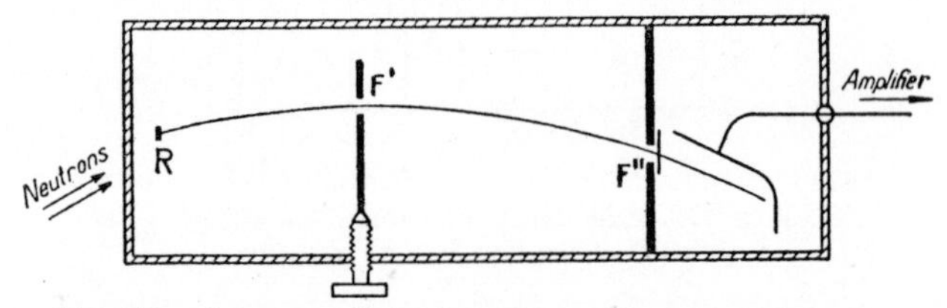

FIG. 48.—Apparatus for measurement of effective charge on fission fragments.

In the first stage of the experiment, the path of the fragments in solid media is studied. Charge equilibrium being very rapidly attained, we may consider that the fragments leaving the layer of uranium are in charge equilibrium with this metal, and in order to attain a charge equilibrium with other materials we must place on the strip of uranium a thin foil which will produce only negligible slowing down of the particles but which will suffice to give attainment of the charge equilibrium.

Fig. 49 shows how the mean effective charge varies with the atomic number of the solid substance through which the particles travelled. It shows a slight decrease as the atomic number grows, from $23 \cdot 5e$ for beryllium to $22e$ for uranium, as far as the heavy group of fission particles is concerned, and from $22e$ to $20e$ in the case of the light group. These results refer to the mean values, but it should be remembered that there are great fluctuations in effective charge from one particle to another within the same group.

In the case of charge equilibrium in gases, studies have been made by filling the first chamber with the gas and varying the pressure.

At very low pressures, there is little charge change between gas and the moving particle, so that the mean effective charge of the latter is the same as if no gas were admitted. With increased pressure, however, the effective charge decreases, passing through a minimum and then slowly increasing again as pressure grows. Figs. 50 and 51 show these changes in the case of argon and hydrogen.

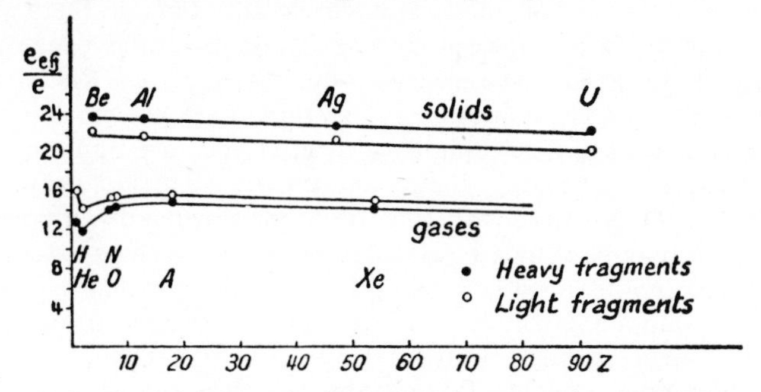

Fig. 49.—Variation of effective charge on fission fragments according to medium traversed.

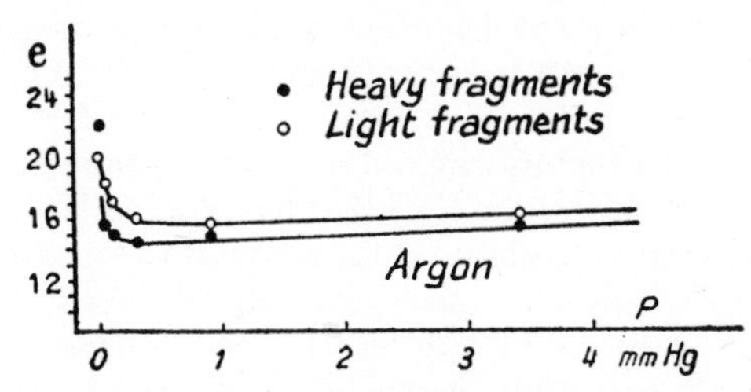

Fig. 50.—Variation in effective charge on fission fragments with pressure in argon.

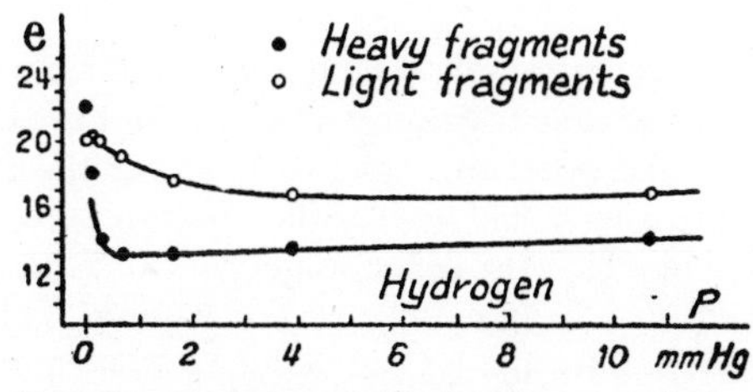

Fig. 51.—Variation of effective charge on fission fragments with pressure in hydrogen.

These results may be explained as follows: the fission fragments as they leave the uranium foil are in equilibrium with the charge in the foil, and they enter the gas. When the pressure is fairly high the charge equilibrium is established with the gas within a short portion of the track (compared with the total track of the particle within the deflection chamber). Under these conditions, the effective charge upon which the magnetic field exerts its force during passage through the chamber is the equilibrium charge corresponding to the velocity of the fragments. Beyond the minimum point the measured charge corresponds to the equilibrium charge which is smaller than that observed in the case of solids. It might be expected that there would then be a step where the equilibrium is attained, after which there would be slight rise. The measured quantity $e_{\text{eff}} = mv/RH$ is measured, and as pressure increases, the value of mv can no longer be considered constant, so that if we neglect the variations in v, we obtain overestimates of e_{eff}, these overestimates being the more marked the higher the pressures. Making use of the slowing-down power of the gas, it may be shown by calculation that no such explanation is valid, and another must be sought. Lassen suggested that the ionized atoms in motion might be able to capture electrons from excited orbits. Normally, such electrons can exist in such orbits only for a very short time, and then fall into the deepest available orbits. The effective section for catching up such an electron in an excited state is greater than that for the capture of an electron in a fundamental state, so that the chance of the loss of charge is greatest at the moment of impact if the electron is excited, while it is less in the case of an electron which has fallen back into a fundamental state. We may imagine, then, that the moving ion will be in a more advanced state of ionization the shorter the time that has elapsed between two successive impacts with the atoms of the medium. Thus, for particles of a given velocity, this interval is inversely proportional to the gas pressure. This explanation can also be used for telling us why the effective charge is markedly greater in solids than in gases.

Equilibrium charges determined at the minimum of the charge-pressure curve are shown in Fig. 49, and they show a slight decrease as Z increases.

When pressure is very small, the charge equilibrium is established only gradually during the trajectory, and may not even be reached if the pressure is sufficiently low. In this last case the effective mean charge turns out to be a function of the relation between the length of the trajectory in which the deflection occurs and the mean distance λ in which the effective charge is decreased by unity. This relationship can be calculated and from it we can deduce λ by means of the experimentally determined values of the effective charge as a function of the pressure. In air and in argon under normal conditions, the λ values for the light and the heavy groups of particles respectively are 3 and 0·4 microns, while in hydrogen they are 90 and 2 microns respectively.

All the measurements in question are for fission fragments with velocities of the order of 10^9 cm./sec. which they acquire at the moment of their production. The experimental difficulties are such that only few studies have been made of the law of variation of charge equilibrium with velocity down to zero speed. However, Lassen[2] has

FIG. 52.—Wilson chamber photograph of trajectories of a pair of fission fragments (kindly supplied by Dr. J. K. Boggild). Median line shows the thin uranium source, seen from the side, and on each side of it the track of a fission fragment. Each track shows diminishing thickness as slowing down occurs. Impacts with nuclei, with projection of atoms, become especially numerous towards the end of each trajectory. The erratic tracks in the emulsion are due to atoms projected by the impact of neutrons from the beam used to bombard the uranium.

shown that for speeds down to about 4×10^8 cm./sec. the charge of the heavy fragment decreases approximately proportionally with speed while that of the light fragment decreases with the value of v^a, where a lies between 0·5 and 1·0.

(3) General Behaviour of Fission Fragments

Because of the high effective charge of fission fragments, the latter have a great ionizing power, this being considerably higher than that for particles or protons of equal velocity (an α-particle of 4 Mev energy is travelling with a speed of $1{\cdot}4 \times 10^9$ cm./sec.). This ionizing power decreases during the slowing down, because of the charge decrease as speed falls off, and if we wish to compare the behaviour of fission fragments with lighter particles we must realize that the corresponding zone with fission fragments is that following the maximum on the ionization curve, where the ionizing power decreases to zero at the end of the track.

In contrast to what happens in the case of the light atomic particles, the projection of atoms from a medium is the cause of but little loss of energy from the fission fragments. The theory of this effect has been developed by Bohr[3], who has shown that to such impacts can be applied formulæ deduced from the elementary theory of corpuscular impacts except in the case of those impacts with small energy transfer or slight particle deflection, in which the interpenetration of the electronic levels around the interacting nuclei upset the simple conception of two particles involved in a normal electrostatic interaction.

In practice, quite different behaviour is found from what we know to be the case with a proton or an α-particle. In particular, we may notice the photograph in Fig. 52, taken with a Wilson cloud chamber, and applying to a fission fragment. The trajectory is seen to be a thick one, because of the density of ionization, and it involves many impacts with other particles, with consequent deflection and ejection of atomic particles, the number of such incidents increasing from the origin to the end of the track. We shall see later that when the fission fragment is sufficiently slowed down, it loses more energy by these impacts than by ionization.

(4) Specific Ionization and Slowing-down Power

Measurements of specific ionization of fission fragments were made by Lassen[4] in various gases, the principle being the same as that employed by various workers in producing Bragg curves for lighter particles. Fig. 53 shows schematically the experimental set-up, which consists of an airtight enclosure in which various gases at various pressures may be introduced. The source of fission fragments is a thin slice of uranium, U, bombarded by slow neutrons. For purposes of collimation there is a plate pierced by cylindrical holes which allow to pass only those fission fragments which are parallel to the axis

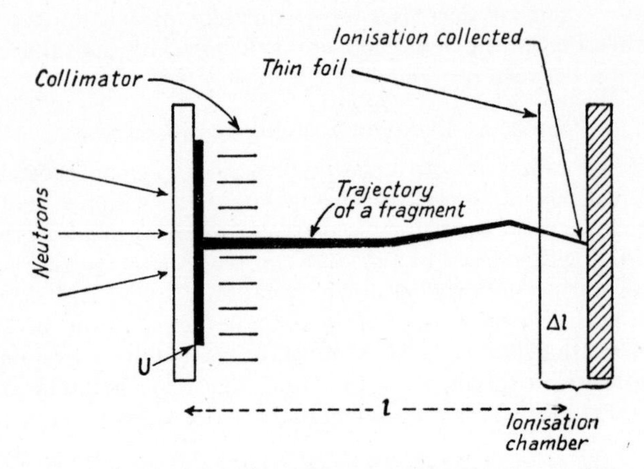

FIG. 53.—Apparatus used by Lassen to measure specific ionization by fission fragments.

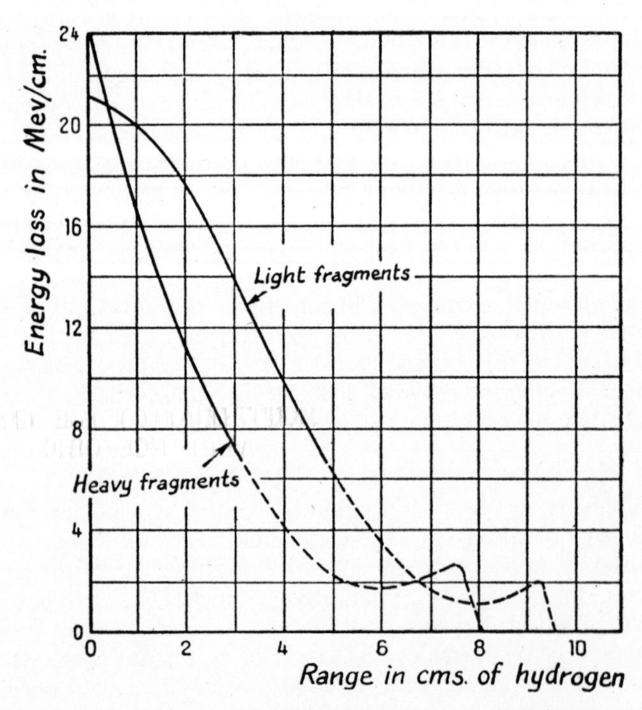

FIG. 54.—Specific ionization by fission fragments in hydrogen, as a function of track length.

of the holes. A flat ionization chamber, the entry face of which is a thin metallic foil, is placed along the path of the beam and is at a distance l from the source and a distance Δl from the foil, this last distance being that in which the ion-pairs are collected. The impulse is amplified. Measurements have been carried out with many gases, and Fig. 54 shows the results obtained with hydrogen under normal conditions. The curves obtained (shown in full lines) have been prolonged into the portions shown by dotted lines, which are calculated from Bohr's theory. Thus each curve consists really of a portion (full line) representing the decelerating power of the gas for the fission fragment, and another part (dotted line) which signifies the portion of the trajectory in which atoms are projected. The general trend of the curves shows that the decelerating power passes through a minimum, showing it to be made up of two factors, one of which is increasing, one decreasing, as the velocity decreases.

Except for a point close to the origin of the fission fragments, the specific ionization of each of the two groups of fragments is markedly different. This makes the measurements possible, as for a given distance from the point of emission of the fragments and up to the position of the ionization chamber, the impulses correspond to the passage of the two groups of fragments, and are grouped around two mean values which are markedly different, and these are associated with the two groups of particles.

(5) Tracks of Fission Fragments

The important deflections suffered by fission fragments give their trajectory the appearance of a broken line, and these breaks cannot be neglected as might be the case with α-particles or protons. Thus we must distinguish between the 'track', which is the full length of path followed by the fragment, and the 'range', which is the distance in a straight line between the origin and the end of the trajectory.

Measurements of the track in gaseous media have been made by methods involving the Wilson cloud chamber, and the results obtained by the Copenhagen group of workers[5] for different gases at 15°C and 1 atmosphere pressure are expressed in mm. in the following table:

	Heavy fragment	Light fragment
Argon	19·4 (0·51)	23·9 (0·63)
Helium	23·0 (0·60)	28·0 (1·00)
Hydrogen	17·7 (0·46)	21·1 (0·55)
Deuterium	18·9 (0·50)	22·5 (0·58)

The figure in brackets in each case shows the ratio between the track of the fragment and that of the α-particle from polonium in the same gas. This ratio is not constant, as can be seen, and shows the variable contribution to the deceleration made by nuclear impact in various gases.

A more recent determination, statistically more accurate, has been made at Saclay[6] where the value for argon was found to be 19·8 and 26·4 for the heavy and light portions respectively.

All the measurements mentioned have been relative to fragments with an original energy equal to that at the time of their emission. In order to trace an energy-track curve, we need values for the relative tracks at other energies. Certain points have been obtained by measuring the tracks starting from some intermediate point in the

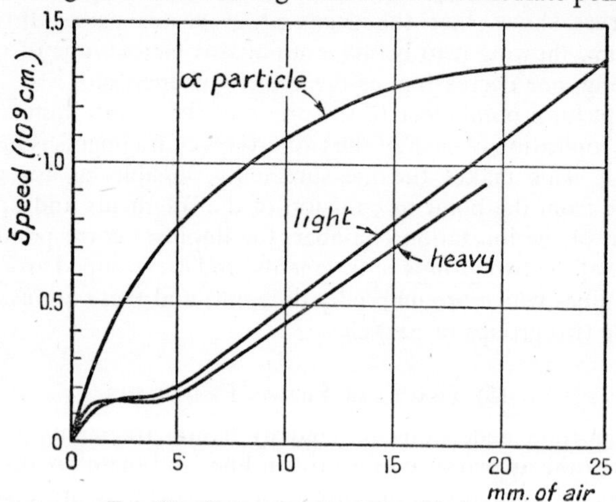

FIG. 55.—Energy-track relationship in air.

trajectory marked by a nuclear collision. The energy E of the fragment after collision is related to the value E' of the atom projected by the expression

$$E = E'\left[\frac{1}{\frac{4mM}{(M+m)^2}\cos^2\theta} - 1\right],$$

and if we can measure E' (actually this is done by measuring the track of the projected atom) and the projection angle θ, then E can be calculated. Actually, the number of experimental points so obtained is very small, and as a result, the energy-track relationship still remains somewhat uncertain.

Bohr has developed his theory by expressing contributions to the decelerating power due to ionization and due to nuclear impacts by formulæ which were fairly approximate, and which, on integration, give the energy-track relationship.

Fig. 55 indicates this result in the case of air.

(6) MEASURING THE RANGE OF THE FISSION FRAGMENTS

Joliot[7] devised a method for measuring the range of fission fragments, specific for a given type of fragments, which can be identified by chemical and radioactive characteristics.

Consider a thin layer of uranium upon a flat support, and arranged above it layers of aluminium foil all of equal thickness (Fig. 56). The whole pile is now submitted to bombardment by thermal neutrons, so that certain atoms are made to undergo fission. The fission fragments issue from an element dS of the surface of the uranium and become localized within the pile at a distance from their point of emission equal to the range P. These fragments have all the same probability of being stopped within any of the aluminium foils, irrespective of which foil is considered, provided the upper face

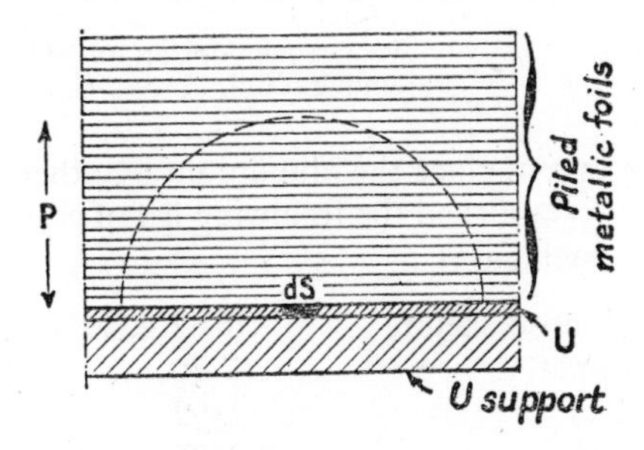

FIG. 56.—Measurement of the range of a fission fragment.

of the foil is at a distance from the point of emission not greater than P, for the emission is isotropic, and the probability is thus proportional to the surface intercepted on a sphere of radius P by the foil of thickness e, this surface being independent of the distance from the plane of the base.

Thus within each foil situated at any distance less than P from the base plane there will be stopped the same number of fission fragments, while this number will fall to zero when the distance is greater than P.

The method is to dissolve the various foils after the irradiation, and from the solution so obtained, one extracts by some suitable chemical method a given element of which the radioactivity can be measured. This radioactivity will be a measure of the number of atoms of that element deposited with the foils.

If now we plot the distance of the foil from the base plane against the measured radioactivity, we get a curve which shows a plateau followed by a rapid drop to zero. Such a curve (Fig. 57) was obtained by Suzor[8] for the isotope 132 of tellurium, a β-active element of half-life 77 hours.

The thickness associated with a reduction of the activity to 50 per cent is the mean range ($3 \cdot 34 \pm 0 \cdot 15$ mg./sq. cm. of aluminium for the example quoted, allowance being made for the slight penetration of the radiation from the uranium) and the zone of decreasing activity enables one to fix the range fluctuation parameter similar to that mentioned in the case of the lighter particles, and this is $0 \cdot 4$ mg./sq. cm. in the example given.

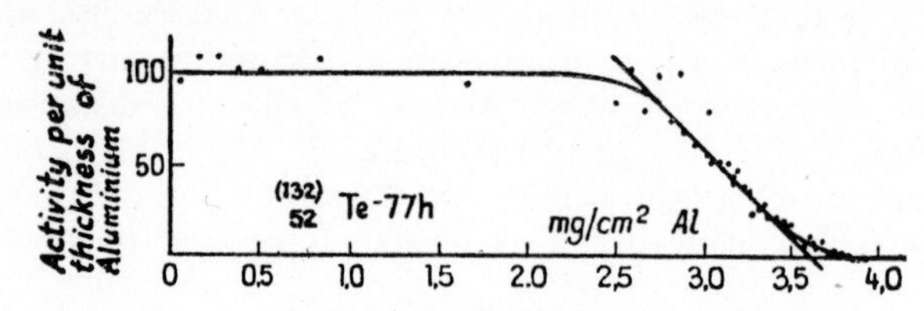

FIG. 57.—Activity-distance relationship for ^{132}Te in aluminium foil.

Naturally, we may replace the aluminium by other materials, and in this way Suzor established the following list of equivalents for 1 g. of aluminium in each case:

Cellulose acetate	0·62 g./sq. cm.
Copper	1·70 „ „
Silver	1·92 „ „
Gold	2·85 „ „

REFERENCES

1. LASSEN, N. O. (1951), *Dan. Mat. Fys. Medd.*, **26**, 5; **26**, 12.
2. LASSEN, N. O. (1949), *Dan. Mat. Fys. Medd.*, **25**, 11.
3. BOHR, N. (1948), *K. danske vidensk. Selsk. Mat. Fys. Medd.*, **18**, 8.
4. LASSEN, N. O. (1946), *Phys. Rev.*, **70**, 577; (1949) **75**, 1762.
5. BOGGILD, J. K., ARROE, O. H., and SIGURGEIRSSON, T. (1947), *Phys. Rev.*, **71**, 281.
6. LABOULAYE, H. DE, TZARA, CH., and OLKOWSKY, J. (1954), *J. de Physique*, **15**, 470.
7. JOLIOT, F. (1944), *Comptes Rendus*, **218**, 488.
8. SUZOR, F. (1949), *Ann. Phys., Paris*, **4**, 269.

Chapter 10

ELECTRONS: GENERAL CONSIDERATIONS AND THEORETICAL RESULTS

(1) GENERAL

The essential character of electrons which prevents an immediate transfer to them of the results obtained with other particles is their small mass. The mass of the electron is 1836 times less than that of the proton, the energy equivalence being 0·511 Mev. This results in the following:

(*a*) At ordinary energies of the order of Mev, the relativity corrections cannot be neglected, and in fact, only for very slow electrons, say below 100 kev energy, can this correction be neglected.

(*b*) In interaction of light atomic particles with electrons, we have seen that the mass difference makes the loss of energy only a very small fraction of the incident energy. This is no longer true when the interacting particles have equal mass, for the whole of the kinetic energy of the incident particle may sometimes then be imparted to the other particle. The principle of uncertainty introduces some effect in this respect, for

(*c*) elastic nuclear interaction such as we have discussed in the case of atomic particles no longer involves appreciable energy loss, because of the great difference in the masses;

(*d*) at the moment of an elastic nuclear interaction, there may be a change of direction of the incident electron, which rebounds from the particle which it strikes. There is also a change of direction when an electronic interaction occurs with transfer to the incident electron of an appreciable part of the energy. Thus, especially at low energies, the track of the electron will be much less rectilinear than that in the case of a heavier particle, and the tracks of electrons are thus very diffuse or devious;

(*e*) a new phenomenon results: there is an emission of braking rays, or *Bremsstrahlung*. The electron arriving within the electrostatic field of a nucleus acquires considerable acceleration from the nucleus, because of its own small mass. Such an acceleration, in classical mechanics, involves the emission of electromagnetic radiation, or in quantum mechanics, of photons. Thus the electron emits some of its kinetic energy in the form of photons. This phenomenon is negligible in the case of heavier atomic particles, but becomes the chief method by which high energy electrons are slowed down.

These remarks applying to the small mass of electrons are valid to both positive electrons or positons, and to negative electrons, sometimes termed negatons. In general, these two types of particles are similar in behaviour, except in one respect. While a negative electron maintains its individuality indefinitely, the positon in any material medium always meets a negative electron forming part of that medium, and mutual annihilation occurs. This phenomenon will be considered in greater detail later.

(2) CONDITIONS OF EMISSION OF ELECTRONS

The conditions for the setting in motion of electrons are as follows:

(*a*) In β radioactivity, an electron is ejected from an atomic nucleus. Contrary to what happens in α radioactivity, the energy imparted to the ejected particle is not sharply defined. If one studies the spectrum of the energies of a β-radioactive material, we find that

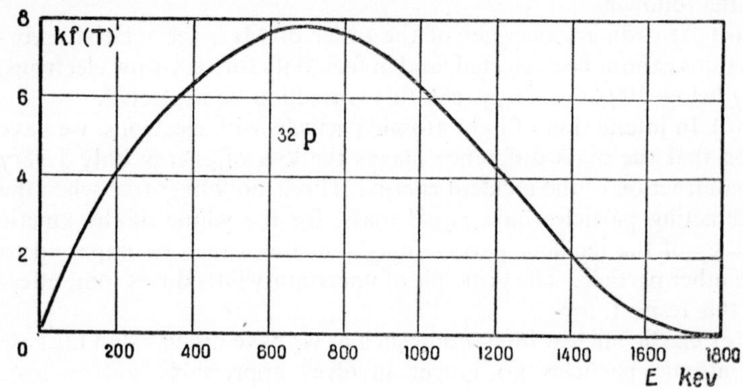

FIG. 58.—β-spectrum for ^{32}P.

the spectrum is continuous, and that the only marked degree of definition is in the maximum energy T_0. The form of the spectrum is quite definite, however, and if dN/N is the proportion of the emitted electrons with a kinetic energy lying between T and $T+dT$, then

$$dN/N = f(T)dT \quad \text{and} \quad \int_0^{T_0} f(T)dT = 1.$$

The function $f(T)$ is characteristic of the radioactive substance being studied. As an example, the graph in Fig. 58 shows that the trend of $f(T)$ has a characteristic shape, given here for the case of the β emission from ^{32}P.

We must remember that the uniformity of energies found as a result of many investigations with α-active materials is not found in the case of the β-radioactive species.

In most cases, the maximum energies of the β spectrum are of the order of several hundred kev or some Mev.

(*b*) The phenomenon of internal conversion is an alternative to the γ emission from nuclei, and this consists in an excited nucleus losing its excitation energy by transferring it to one of the electrons of the orbits outside the nucleus. In such a case, the kinetic energy with which this electron is ejected is equal to the excitation energy minus the binding energy corresponding to the position occupied by the expelled electron. For a given excitation energy, there are only possible, then, a few limited values of energies for the conversion electrons, each corresponding to the level from which the electron has been expelled.

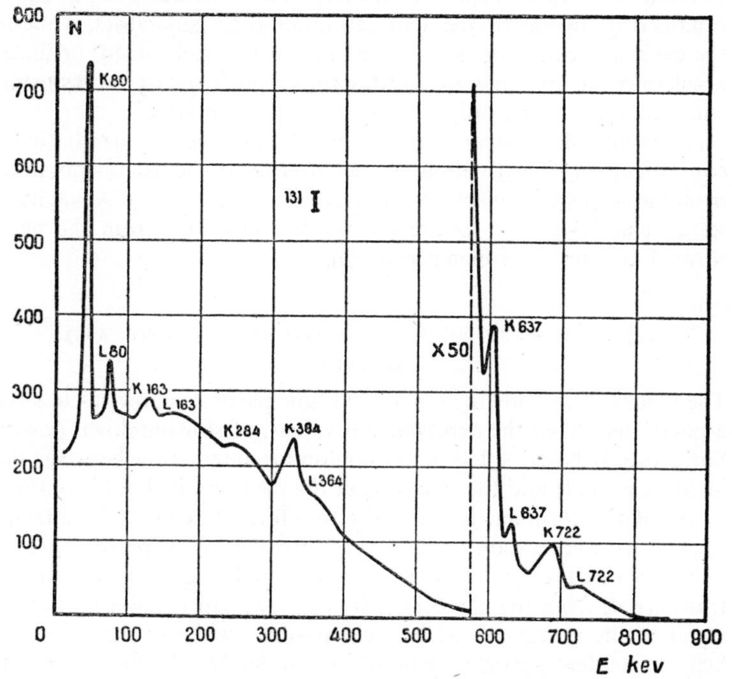

FIG. 59.—Spectrum of β conversion rays from ^{131}I.

In measuring the spectrum of a β-active substance, we find often that there is superposition on the continuous spectrum of energy peaks, quite well defined, and corresponding to the conversion rays. This means that β radioactivity often leaves the nucleus in an excited state and that the de-excitation produces the emission of the conversion electrons. Fig. 59 shows, for example, the spectrum of electrons emitted from ^{131}I.

(*c*) Internal materialization occurs when, as a result of the laws of exclusion, a nucleus in an excited energy state above 1·022 Mev can lose its energy neither by emission of γ radiation, nor by internal conversion. In this case, the excitation energy is emitted as a pair of electrons of opposite sign, formed at the expense of this energy, which absorbs thus $2mc^2 = 1 \cdot 022$ Mev, the total kinetic energy being equal to the balance.

(*d*) The various interaction effects from the action of photons on matter, which will be dealt with later, result sometimes in the setting into motion of electrons from the shells of the atoms of the medium, and sometimes in creation, within the electric field of the nucleus, of electron-pairs, by materialization.

(*e*) Many types of accelerators have been used for the acceleration of electrons, and the beams, with energies of some Mev, can be easily obtained by means of the Van de Graaff type generators, while in the case of accelerators such as the betatron, synchrotron, or linear accelerator, many hundreds of Mev can be imparted to the electrons, while energies of the order of 1 Gev are now possible.

(*f*) Beams of positive electrons may be obtained by irradiating a convenient source with photons, the latter being themselves obtained from the stopping of electron beams from an accelerator. A magnetic set-up enables one to isolate the positive electrons from the pairs formed as a result of materialization.

(3) Slowing down of Electrons by Ionization and Excitation

The theory of the slowing down of atomic particles allows us to have a good idea, from the experimental values, of slowing-down power. Since this is based solely upon coulombic interaction between the incident particle and the electrons of the medium, it should conform to the Bethe formula, but actually this formula cannot be directly applied without certain modifications, for the following reasons:

(i) Because the masses involved are of equal magnitude, the energy transferred, from the classical point of view, can reach a maximum equal to the energy of the incident particle, while in the case of a heavier incident particle it cannot exceed $4m/M \ll 1$. In actual fact, when two electrons collide, it is impossible to know after the impact which of the two particles in motion was originally moving and which was the static one. This is not purely a question of the ability to distinguish them, but involves the much more profound philosophy of the principle of uncertainty, by virtue of which, when two particles of the same kind interact together, they become no longer distinguishable. It is conventional, then, to assume that the electron which was originally in motion is, after impact, the one which has the greater energy, and the maximum energy which can be transferred is not T, but $\frac{1}{2}T$.

(ii) If we apply the Pauli principle to the case of two electrons which collide, they cannot be in the same quantum state, and this is a condition which is not invoked in the case of collisions in which the incident particle is not an electron.

(iii) With atomic particles, slowing down is involved in many phenomena such as ionization and excitation, in which the transferred energy is small compared with the total energy of the incident particle. As a result, if we compare the losses of energy for particles of various types, but of the same energy, in passing through the same thicknesses of a material medium, we find these energy losses are distributed according to a gaussian law, in which the statistical results of many identical elementary phenomena are considered. Thus, the mean loss of energy becomes the most probable energy loss.

It is otherwise with electrons. During a single interaction, the energy loss may attain a high value, equal, at the maximum, to half the incident energy. On the other hand, it may be shown that the mean effective section for energy loss, being smaller than the incident energy, is very large. This has been shown to be the case in non-relativistic classical theory, and also holds for more elaborate instances.

As a result, if an electron traverses a given thickness of a medium, we may consider the numerous collisions with small energy loss, which if occurring individually would give rise, for a given energy loss, to a gaussian distribution, but to these must be added the less frequent collisions involving larger energy loss, and for which the gaussian law must be replaced by a more complicated probability law with a bias towards the greater energy losses.

Thus, in the case of electrons, the mean energy loss, and the most probable energy loss, during passage through a given thickness of matter, will not be identical.

(4) Mean Energy Loss During Ionization and Excitation

The theory developed essentially by Möller and Bethe[1, 2] leads to the value of the mean energy loss as follows:

$$\Delta T_m = \xi \left[\log \frac{mv^2 T}{2I^2(1-\beta^2)} + \tfrac{1}{8} + (\tfrac{9}{8} + \log 2)(1-\beta^2) - (\tfrac{1}{4} + 2\log 2)(1-\beta^2)^{\frac{1}{2}} \right].$$

m, v, T = mass, velocity, and kinetic energy of the electron

$$\xi = \frac{2\pi e^4}{mv^2} NZ\Delta x = \pi r^2 . NZ\Delta x \cdot \frac{2}{\beta^2} \cdot mc^2$$

N = number of atoms per unit volume of the medium

Z = number of electrons per atom of the medium

Δx = length of the element of trajectory considered

$r = e^2/mc^2 = 2{\cdot}82 \times 10^{-13}$ cm. or the classical electron radius

I = mean ionization potential of the atoms in the medium, as defined in Chapter 5.

In the case of a speed to which relativity considerations do not apply, i.e. for $\beta = 0$, and $T = \frac{1}{2}mv^2$, the formula becomes

$$T_m = 2\xi . \log \left[\sqrt{\left(\frac{e}{2}\right)} \cdot \frac{T}{I} \right],$$

where e is the base of the Napierian logarithms.

If now we express the energies in Mev, ξ has the value

$$\xi = 2 \cdot 55 \times 10^{-25} \frac{NZ\Delta x}{\beta^2}.$$

It may also be shown that

$$\frac{mv^2 T}{2I^2(1-\beta^2)} = \frac{T}{2I^2 mc^2} \cdot \frac{m^2 c^2 v^2}{1-\beta^2} = \frac{T}{2I^2 mc^2} T(T+2mc^2),$$

so that one may also write

$$\Delta T_m = \xi \left[2\log \frac{T}{I} + \log \left(1 + \frac{T}{2mc^2}\right) + f(\beta) \right]$$

and

$$f(\beta) = 0 \cdot 125 + 1 \cdot 818(1-\beta^2) - 1 \cdot 636(1-\beta^2)^{\frac{1}{2}}.$$

Fig. 60 shows the variation of $f(\beta)$ with β. It will be seen that this function decreases from $0 \cdot 307$ when β is zero, to $-0 \cdot 244$ when β is $0 \cdot 88$, and increases then until it reaches the value $0 \cdot 175$ when β is unity. Thus, a formula based upon the same considerations as the formula for slowing down of heavy particles cannot be made applicable when T is not markedly greater than I, and as a result, the value of $2\log(T/I)$ is equal to several units, and the term $f(\beta)$ becomes only a correction term of small significance.

If the formula is now compared with that of Bethe in the case of the proton (see formula 1, Chapter 5), it can be easily seen that the latter can be written in the form

$$\Delta T_m = \xi \left[2\log \frac{(m/M)T}{I} + 2\log \left(1 + \frac{T}{2mc^2}\right) + f'(\beta) \right],$$

where ξ represents the same quantity as before, m and M being the masses of the electron and the proton, so that

$$f'(\beta) = 4\log 2 - 2\beta^2.$$

For equal velocities of the electron and proton, the first terms in the bracket become identical, while the second terms differ by a factor of 2, but since they are in most cases much smaller than the first terms, there results but little difference, and the same applies to the third terms.

As a result, to a first approximation, we may say that the slowing-down power for an electron is the same as that for a proton of the same velocity. It passes through a minimum for an energy value close to $2mc^2$, i.e. 1 Mev below the figure at which the decrease is essentially conditioned by the term $1/\beta^2$ in the expression for ξ, and above that at which, β being virtually constant, we see an increase due to the logarithmic term. The essential difference from the case of heavy particles is that $2mc^2$ corresponds, in the case of electrons, to normal energies.

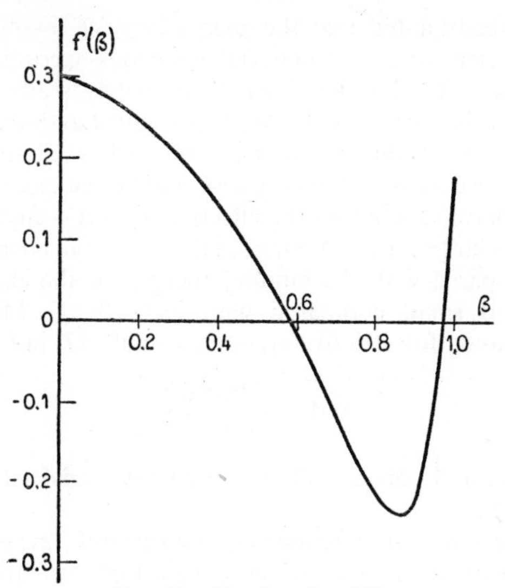

FIG. 60.—The function $f(\beta)$.

The logarithmic growth from the minimum is, as in the case of the heavy particles, disturbed by the effect of the polarization of the medium which tends to limit it.

It will be noted that the formula can be put into the form of the slowing-down power of the traversed medium, i.e.

$$\frac{\Delta T_m}{\Delta x} = \frac{\xi}{\Delta x}\left[2\log\frac{T}{I}+\log\left(1+\frac{T}{2mc^2}\right)+f(\beta)\right]$$

or of the atomic slowing-down power

$$S = \frac{1}{N}\cdot\frac{\Delta T_m}{\Delta x},$$

or as the slowing-down power per electron,

$$\frac{S}{Z} = \frac{1}{NZ}\cdot\frac{\Delta T_m}{\Delta x}$$

and

$$\frac{S}{Z} = \frac{\xi}{NZ\Delta x}\left[2\log\frac{T}{I}+\log\left(1+\frac{T}{2mc^2}\right)+f(\beta)\right]$$

$$= \frac{2\cdot 55\times 10^{-25}}{\beta^2}\left[2\log\frac{T}{I}+\log\left(1+\frac{T}{2mc^2}\right)+f(\beta)\right] \text{Mev.cm}^2.$$

(5) Distribution of Energy Loss and Most Probable Energy Loss

We have already noted that the energy loss ΔT involved in transit through an element Δx of material fluctuates according to a non-gaussian law. This law has been theoretically studied by various workers, and, in particular, by Williams[3] and Landau[4].

According to Williams, ionizations and excitations may be classified according to the energy lost, and the calculations of Bethe and Möller have shown that the effective section is smaller when the energy loss is larger. In particular, in the case of an energy loss which is large compared with the binding energies of the electrons in the medium, and small compared with $mc^2 = 0\cdot 511$ Mev, then the classical formula for effective section (formula 17, in Chapter 2)

$$d\sigma = \frac{2\pi e^4}{mv^2}\frac{dE}{E^2}$$

is applicable, and corresponds to an energy transfer lying between E and $E+dE$.

Williams classifies interactions into two groups: one group consists of the frequent interactions which have a high probability of being produced several times in the course of a portion of trajectory Δx, and a group of interactions which are rare and have but small chance of occurring during the course of this same element of trajectory Δx. While this classification is quite arbitrary, this is a completely unimportant consideration as far as results are concerned, and it is convenient to define the energy ξ such that all transfer of energy smaller than this value will belong to the first group, and larger transfers will fall into the second group. Thus, ξ is the mean energy of an electron traversing Δx, suffering but one single energy transfer greater than ξ. Thus, ξ can be given by the expressions

$$\int_{\xi}^{\infty}\frac{2\pi e^4}{mv^2}\cdot\frac{dE}{E^2}\cdot NZ\Delta x = \frac{2\pi e^4}{mv^2}\cdot\frac{NZ\Delta x}{\xi} = 1,$$

$$\xi = \frac{2\pi e^4}{mv^2}\cdot NZ\Delta x,$$

which give some physical significance to the quantity ξ.

If the collisions all belonged to the first group ($E < \xi$) we would have a quasi-gaussian distribution of the energy losses. A formula due to Bethe indicates that, if we consider only energy losses corresponding to individual processes in which the transfer of energy is equal to or smaller than W, then the mean value, which is also the most probable value since we neglect great losses, is

$$\Delta T_p = \xi\left(\log\frac{2mv^2 W}{I^2(1-\beta^2)} - \beta^2\right),$$

and in the case when $W = \xi$, we have

$$\Delta T_p = \xi\left(\log\frac{2mv^2 \xi}{I^2(1-\beta^2)} - \beta^2\right).$$

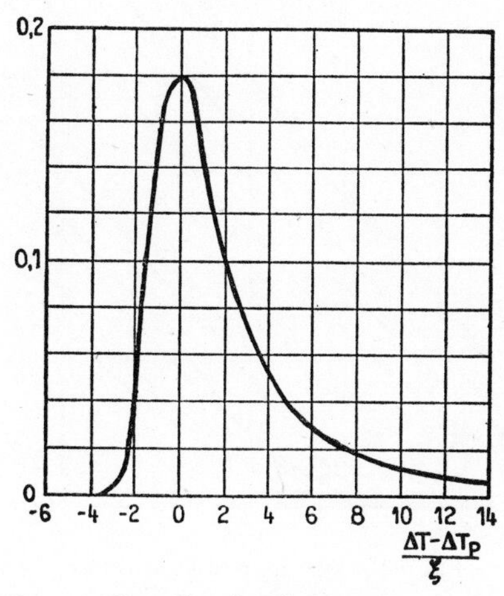

FIG. 61.—Landau curve.

If now we no longer neglect the losses of energy greater than ξ, it can be shown (Williams) that the most probable energy loss is given by simply using the value $0 \cdot 30\xi$ in the foregoing expression.

Landau has treated the problem in a somewhat different way, rather more rigorous in treatment, but he arrives at conclusions which are very similar, and his expression for the most probable energy loss is as follows:

$$\Delta T_p = \xi\left(\log\frac{2mv^2 \xi}{I^2(1-\beta^2)} - \beta^2 + 0 \cdot 37\right).$$

Landau also obtained the distribution curve for energy losses shown in Fig. 61. By measurement of the squares and taking the width of the curve-enclosed area at middle-height, we find that this width is $3 \cdot 98\xi$, or practically 4ξ.

(6) Effect of the Density of the Medium

The correction due to the effect of density of the medium has been studied by many workers from the theoretical point of view. The most recent calculations are due to Sternheimer[5]. Fig. 62 shows, for various media, the value of the correction which must be introduced into the formula for decelerating power in order to take this into

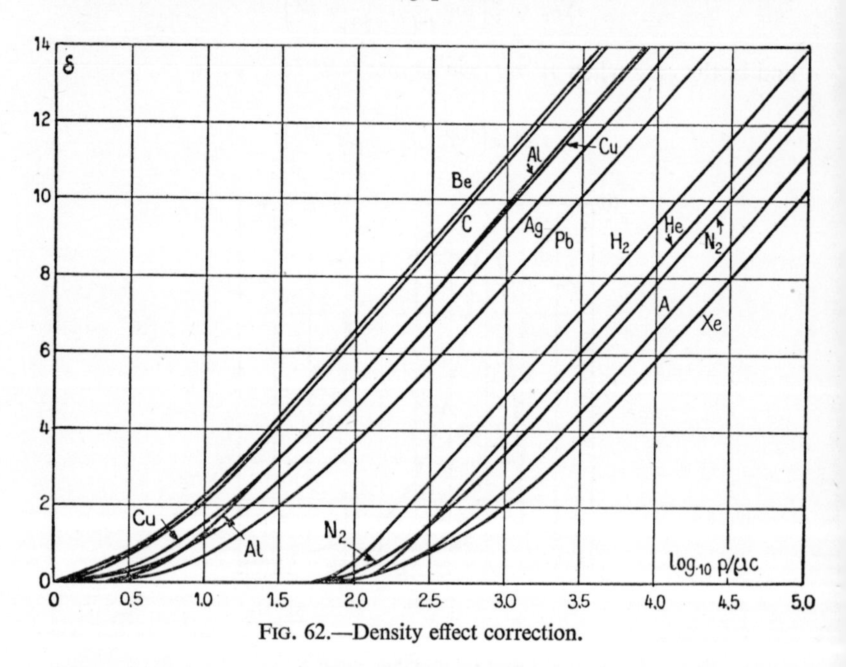

Fig. 62.—Density effect correction.

account. This correction is applicable whatever the nature of the moving particle. It assumes that the decelerating power has been expressed in the form

$$\frac{\Delta T}{\Delta x} = \frac{\xi}{\Delta x} A$$

when no account has been taken of the correction, and when the correction has been applied, it becomes

$$\frac{\Delta T}{\Delta x} = \frac{\xi}{\Delta x}(A - \delta).$$

Figures 63 and 64 show how, according to Sternheimer, the density effect decreases the deceleration by ionization in the case of electrons when the media are gases or solids. According to Goldwasser, Mills

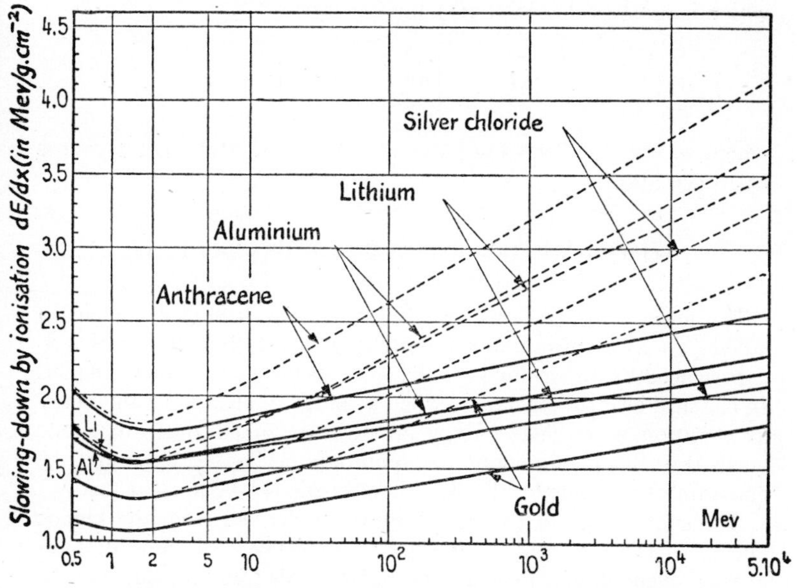

FIG. 63.—Slowing-down power for electrons in various solids.

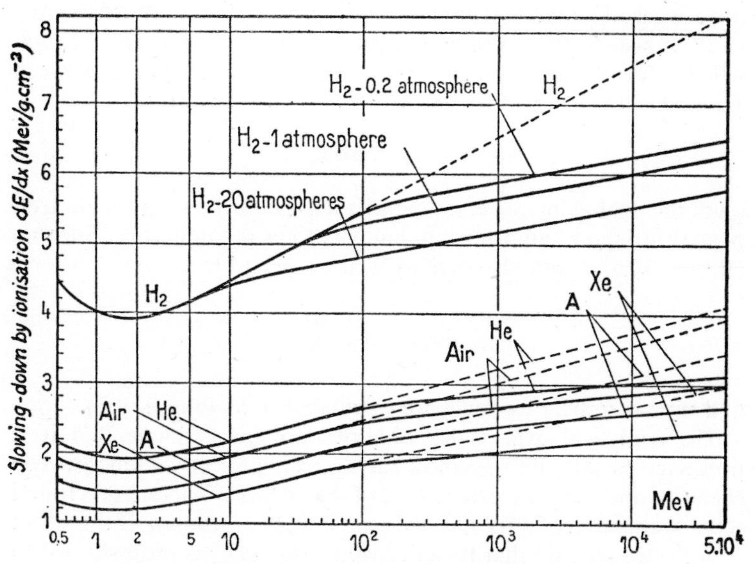

FIG. 64.—Slowing-down power for electrons in various gases.

and Hanson[6] the loss of energy tends towards the asymptotic value which is most probable at very high energies,

$$\Delta T_p = \xi\left[\log\frac{\Delta x}{a_0}+0\cdot 37\right],$$

where $a_0 = 5\cdot 29\times 10^{-9}$ cm., the radius of the Bohr orbit in the hydrogen atom.

(7) Deceleration by Emission of Braking Rays (Bremsstrahlung)

When an electron passes into an electric field around a nucleus, it suffers an acceleration much more significant than that which is experienced by an atomic particle, since its mass is so much smaller. In classical electromagnetism, when a charge of electricity undergoes acceleration, it radiates energy in the form of an electromagnetic wave. For this phenomenon, the quantum mechanics substitutes the emission of photons by the passing electrons in the nuclear field.

The energy carried by these photons is derived from the kinetic energy of the electrons, which are thus deprived of some of their energy, even though this may be but a small fraction, but may be large also.

The maximum energy which an electron can lose during this braking action is equal to its kinetic energy T. Bethe and Heitler[7] have worked out the theory for this phenomenon. A differential effective section $\mathrm{d}\sigma_E$ of radiation for the atoms forming the medium which is traversed and for emission of an energy photon lying between E and $E+\mathrm{d}E$ $(0 < E < T)$ can be considered such that

$$\mathrm{d}\varpi_E = n\,\mathrm{d}\sigma_E$$

gives the probability of emission of such a photon when an electron passes through a thin foil containing n atoms per unit area. Such an effective section can also equally well be given by

$$\mathrm{d}\sigma_E = \sigma(E)\frac{\mathrm{d}E}{T}$$

and the theoretical formulæ are calculated so as to give $\sigma(E)$.

The analytical expressions obtained are quite simple, but it is necessary to take into account the screening effect caused between electrons and the electrostatic field of the nucleus. This effect is found to be proportional to the atomic number of the medium. If this effect is neglected we find that the effective section $\sigma(E)$ is proportional to the square of the nuclear charge. In this way we can express $\sigma(E)$ in a way which is independent of the nature of the slowing-down atoms, the unit of effective section being taken as a quantity proportional to Z^2. Theory suggests that this unit should be

$$\bar{\sigma} = \frac{Z^2}{137}\left(\frac{e^2}{mc^2}\right)^2 = \frac{Z^2}{137}r^2$$

$$= \frac{Z^2(2\cdot 82\times 10^{-13})^2}{137} = Z^2\times 5\cdot 81\times 10^{-28}\,\text{cm}^2.$$

Fig. 65 shows the quantity $\frac{E}{W}\cdot\frac{\sigma(E)}{\bar{\sigma}}$ for various electron energies.

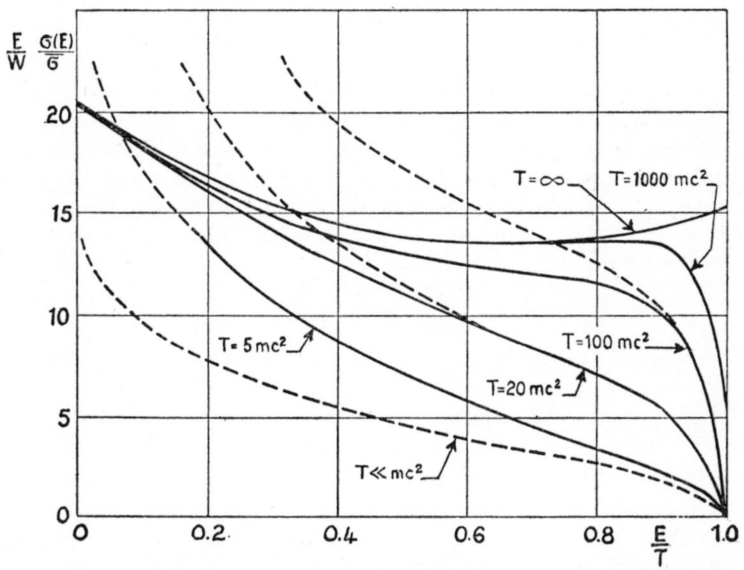

FIG. 65.—Differential effective cross-section for energy loss by radiation for an electron of kinetic energy T ($W = T+mc^2$).

In this expression, E is the energy carried by the photon, and as a result $E\sigma(E)$ is proportional to the total energy carried by the photons of energy E, and W is the total energy $T+mc^2$ of the incident electron. The curves shown in dotted lines are those obtained when the screen effect is neglected, and they are applicable to all atoms. The curves in full lines refer to the effective sections corrected for the screen effect, and these have been calculated for lead and are valid only for this one element. The screening effect being more important as Z increases and the photon energy decreases, the curves relating to atoms with low Z values (below 82) lie between those of lead and the curves without any screen effect.

From these curves we see that the energy radiated by the electron is radiated in the form of low energy photons.

Now we may consider the mean energy lost by radiation by an electron passing through a thickness Δx of material containing N atoms per c.c. This will be

$$\Delta T_m = \int_0^T \mathrm{d}\varpi_E = N\Delta x \int_0^T \frac{E\sigma(E)\mathrm{d}E}{T}.$$

It is convenient to remember that this mean energy loss is related to the total energy of the incident electron by the expression

$$\frac{\Delta T_m}{W} = N\Delta x \int_0^T \frac{E\sigma(E)\mathrm{d}E}{TW}.$$

The integral of the second number is proportional to the area of the curve corresponding to the figure, and it may be seen that the fraction of energy of the electron which is radiated during passage through a foil of chosen thickness varies as a factor which is relatively small when the energy of the electron increases. From this relation $\Delta T_m/W$ it is usual to define an effective section for radiation by the formula

$$\frac{\Delta T_m}{W} = N\sigma_{\mathrm{rad}}\Delta x$$

or

$$\sigma_{\mathrm{rad}} = \int_0^T \frac{E.\sigma(E).\mathrm{d}E}{TW}.$$

If there is no screening effect, then the variation of σ_{rad} expressed in terms of $\overline{\sigma}$ would be the same for all atoms. Fig. 66 shows the law of variation calculated when we take into consideration the screening effect, as Heitler has deduced. It is seen that the variation of σ_{rad} is only by a factor of about 3 from one end to the other in the energy range.

At high energies, σ_{rad} becomes constant. This means that on the average an electron radiates the same fraction of its energy per unit of length, and we call 'radiation length' the distance (L) over which the electron suffers an energy decrease by the fraction ratio e due to radiation. Because of the constancy of σ_{rad} and of the fact that, at high energies, T and W may be confused, the energy of the electron decreases on the average as a function of the path x according to an exponential law

$$T = T_0 e^{-N\sigma_{\mathrm{rad}}x},$$

so that the radiation length will be given by

$$L = \frac{1}{N\sigma_{\mathrm{rad}}}.$$

We shall see later that for the range of energies here considered, the deceleration due to radiation is practically the only one of importance.

Given here, and due to Rossi and Greisen[8], but corrected by Bethe and Ashkin[9], are the L values for various media, expressed in g./sq. cm.:

H_2	He	C	N_2	O_2	Al	A	Fe	Cu	Pb	air	water
58	85	42·5	38	34·2	23·9	19·4	13·8	12·8	5·8	36·5	35·9

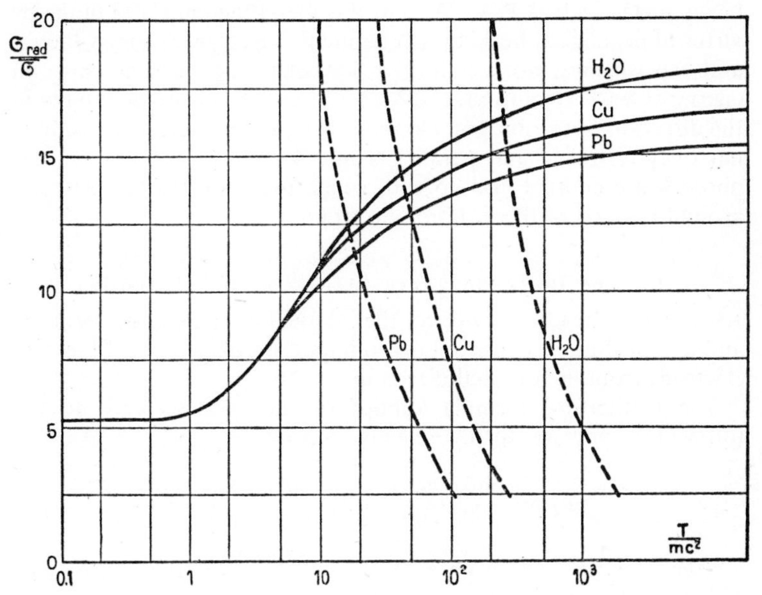

FIG. 66.—Variation of effective cross-section of radiation with energy.

In Fig. 66 are given in broken lines the contributions to the deceleration of electrons by ionization in various media, expressed in the same way as for the braking effect.

The cross-section for ionization is given by

$$\sigma_{\text{ion}} = \frac{1}{nW} \cdot \frac{\Delta T}{\Delta x} = \frac{S}{W}.$$

Since the decelerating power varies little at energies which are sufficiently great, the term σ_{ion} varies somewhat because of the inverse function of W. On the figure we give $\sigma_{\text{ion}}/\bar{\sigma}$ also. For each element there is a 'critical energy' which separates the zone of low energies, in which ionization and excitation are essential factors in deceleration, from the zone of high energy where the braking action becomes important. The critical energy is lower in the case of media with high

Z values. Here are given the values in Mev for some media, due to the same authors:

H_2	He	C	N_2	O_2	Al	A	Fe	Cu	Pb	air	water
340	220	103	87	77	47	34·5	24	21·5	6·9	83	93

The Bremsstrahlen are used as a source of photons in apparatus employed for the acceleration of electrons. The beam of electrons which have been accelerated is allowed to fall upon a target of some heavy metal such as Pt or W, and this metal then emits photons by virtue of the nuclear braking effect upon the electrons. Theory shows, and experimental work confirms, that when the electrons have an energy at least equal to several Mev, the emission is preferentially in the direction of the incident electrons. As, in practice, it is usually a narrowly restricted and parallel beam which strikes the target, the photons are emitted in a cone of small angle (only a few degrees) around the axis of the beam of electrons.

(8) Elastic Deviation of Electrons by Electrons

As we have already mentioned, the interaction of electrons with the ambient medium is likely to lead to important deviations of incident electrons from the original direction.

The Rutherford formula applied in such a case leads to the following expression for the effective section:

$$d\sigma_\Omega = \frac{4e^4}{m^2 V^4} \cdot \frac{\cos\phi}{\sin^4\phi} d\Omega = \frac{4r^2}{\beta^4} \cdot \frac{\cos\phi}{\sin^4\phi} d\Omega$$

for the deviation within an angle ϕ, the deviation angle being $d\Omega$. This formula is not relativistic, and takes no account of the exclusion principle and the principle of uncertainty.

A more correct formula, devised by Möller, is

$$d\sigma_\Omega = \frac{2r^2}{\beta^4 \sin\phi} \cdot \frac{\gamma+1}{\gamma^2} \left[\frac{4}{(1-\mu^2)^2} - \frac{3}{1-\mu^2} + \frac{(\gamma-1)^2}{4\gamma^2} \left\{ 1 + \frac{4}{1-\mu^2} \right\} \right] d\Omega$$

with

$$\gamma = \frac{1}{\sqrt{(1-\beta^2)}} \qquad \mu = \cos\alpha = \frac{2-(\gamma+3)\sin^2\phi}{2+(\gamma-1)\sin^2\phi},$$

where α is the deviation angle, in the system of which the mass is the centre.

When this formula is developed with relation to β, it takes the form

$$d\sigma_\Omega = \frac{4r^2}{\beta^4} \frac{\cos\phi}{\sin^4\phi} \{(1+\tan^4\phi+\tan^2\phi) - \beta^2(4+3\tan^4\phi-2\tan^2\phi-3\sin^2\phi\tan^2\phi)\ldots\} d\Omega,$$

and it may be seen that when β and ϕ are very small, we are back again to the Rutherford formula.

In fact, the curve traced is that relating to nuclear deviation, but it can be easily seen that the two formulæ are very similar at small

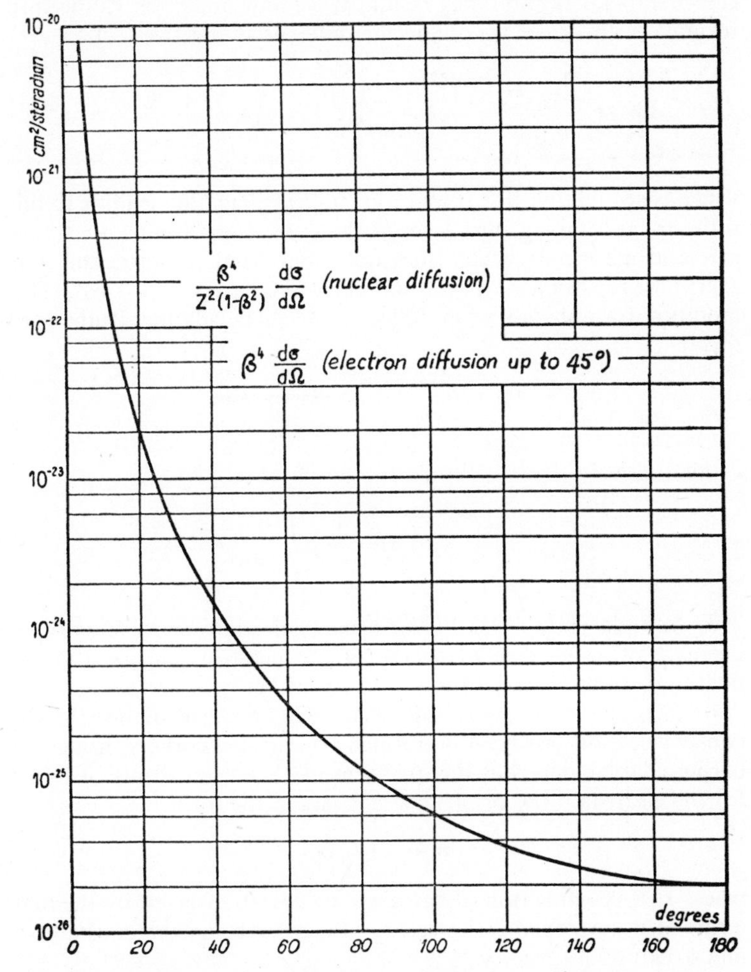

FIG. 67.—Rutherford formula for electron diffusion on electrons and nuclei.

angles. By virtue of the convention relating to choice of the electron which is to be considered the primary one, the deviation cannot be considered to occur except between 0° and 45°, and in this region the two formulæ may be taken as practically identical. Fig. 67 shows the variation as a function of ϕ of the Rutherford effective section.

(9) Elastic Nuclear Deviation of Electrons

The passage of an electron into the coulombic field of a nucleus, apart from emission of Bremsstrahlung, is made practically without energy loss because of the great mass difference. On the other hand, considerable deflection may result. If we now apply the Rutherford formula in this case, we obtain the differential effective section

$$d\sigma_{\Omega} = \frac{Z^2 e^4}{4m^2 v^4}\frac{1}{\sin^4\frac{\phi}{2}}d\Omega = \frac{Z^2 r^2}{4\beta^4}\frac{1}{\sin^4\frac{\phi}{2}}d\Omega \qquad \left(\frac{r^2}{4} = 1{\cdot}99\times 10^{-26}\ \text{cm}^2\right)$$

which is not relativistic. If we revert to the calculation leading to this formula, and taking into account the corrections for relativity, we arrive at a formula which does not differ from the preceding one except for replacement of m by the relativistic mass $m/(1-\beta^2)^{\frac{1}{2}}$. This modified formula, in what follows, we shall call the Rutherford formula

$$d\sigma_R = \frac{Z^2 r^2}{4}\cdot\frac{1-\beta^2}{\beta^4}\cdot\frac{1}{\sin^4\frac{\phi}{2}}\cdot d\Omega,$$

or alternatively,

$$d\sigma_R = \frac{Z^2 r^2}{4}\left(\frac{mc^2}{cp}\right)^2\left(\frac{W}{cp}\right)^2\cdot\frac{d\Omega}{\sin^4\frac{\phi}{2}}.$$

This formula shows clearly the usual deflection characters: rapid decrease of a function of energy of the incident particle and the deflection angle. Fig. 67 shows this variation.

In fact, this formula is still insufficient, and calculation of the effective section has been performed by various workers, using not corpuscular models, but the quantum mechanics concepts of Dirac for the electron. The result then appears in the form

$$d\sigma = d\sigma_R . f(\phi),$$

where $f(\phi)$ is a function of the angle of deviation given by the first terms of a developed series relative to αZ, α being the constant of fine structure,

$$\alpha = \frac{2\pi e^2}{hc} = \frac{1}{137}.$$

Mott[10] has given the expression for $f(\phi)$, which after slight modification by McKinley and Feshbach[11] becomes

$$f(\phi) = 1-\beta^2\sin^2\frac{\phi}{2}+Z\alpha . \pi\beta\sin\frac{\phi}{2}\left(1-\sin\frac{\phi}{2}\right)+\ldots$$

In fact, these last authors have given the series development as far as the term $Z^4\alpha^4$, but the preceding approximation may be considered as sufficient for values of β near unity, and for $Z \leqslant 25$. The formula applies to negative electrons, but in the case of positons it is necessary to replace the Z by $-Z$.

In the case of electrons which are not very rapidly moving, where $Z > 25$, the approximation given is insufficient, and we must invoke the use of subsequent terms in the expanded series. In practice we make use of tables of numerical values and the curves for $f(\phi)$.

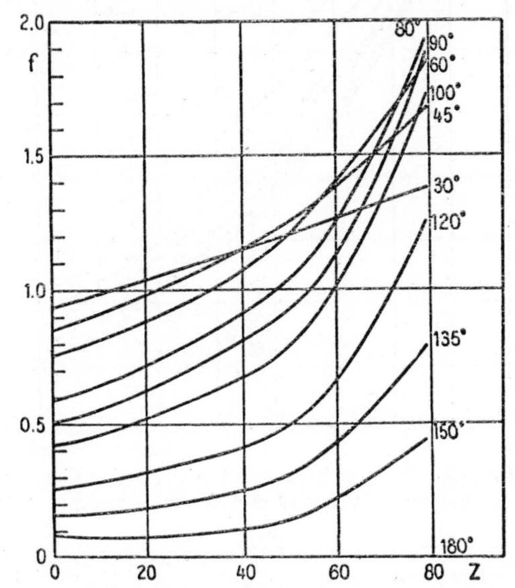

FIG. 68.—Correction to Rutherford formula for nuclear deflection of electrons of energy at least 4 Mev.

By way of example, Fig. 68 gives the variation of $f(\phi)$ for negative electrons of 4 Mev or above. It will be seen that for light nuclei the effective cross-section is decreased, especially for high angles ϕ, while for heavy nuclei it increases for small angles and becomes smaller at large angles. Fig. 69 gives, for the same energies, the relationship between the effective sections for positons and those for electrons[12], and it shows that the positons are less deflected than negatons, this comparison being more important when we consider great angles of deflection and heavier deflecting nuclei. Analytically, this involves a transposition of $-Z$ for the Z when positons are considered in place of negatons.

At non-relativistic energies, the preceding considerations cease to be valid, as it is necessary to take into account the screening effect of the extra-nuclear electrons, and this effect is not negligible. The problem has been tackled by Molière[13], and the result is given in Fig. 70, where $f(\phi)$ is expressed in terms of the ratio ϕ/ϕ_0 for various

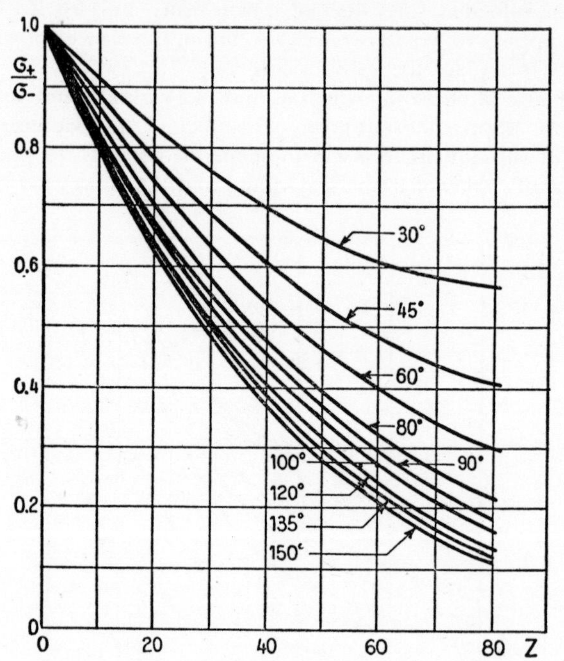

FIG. 69.—Relation between effective cross-section for nuclear deflection of positons and negatons.

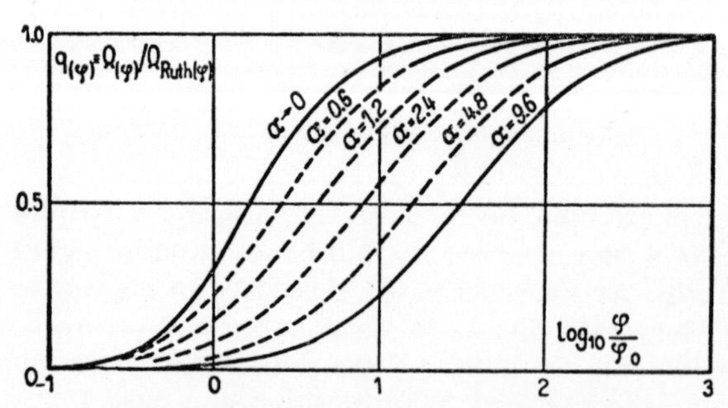

FIG. 70.—Molière correction for screening effect.

values of the parameter $\alpha = Z/137\beta$, ϕ_0 being defined by the expression

$$\phi_0^{(\mathrm{rad})} = \frac{Z^{\frac{1}{3}}}{137}\cdot\frac{mc^2}{cp} = \frac{3\cdot 74\times 10^3\times Z^{\frac{1}{3}}}{cp}$$

in which p is the amount of electron movement and cp is expressed in ev ($cp = T^{\frac{1}{2}}(T+2mc^2)^{\frac{1}{2}}$).

At high energies, when the wavelength $\lambda = h/p$ of the electron becomes of the order of magnitude of the nuclei of the deflecting material, we cannot consider this as a point charge, and we must then take into consideration the distribution of charge at its interior. Experimental[14] and theoretical[15] studies, concerned with the nuclear dispersion of electrons of energies 125 and 150 Mev, have recently been undertaken, and appear to throw new light on the way in which the proton charges are located in the nucleus. By means of the linear electron accelerator at Stanford University (U.S.A.), which gives a 600-Mev beam, and the various accelerators which will have powers in the vicinity of 1 Gev, extension of researches to regions of much higher energies should be possible.

It should be noted that the effective section for nuclear deflection is Z^2 times greater than that for electronic deflection. As a result, with the exception of light media, the nuclear deflection is always more important than the electronic deflection, and this overwhelming effect is even more marked when the action occurs in media consisting of heavy atoms.

(10) Multiple Deflection

In practice, when an electron traverses a thickness δ of matter, it undergoes a certain number of interactions, each of which induces a deflection quite independently of the ones which preceded it. As a result, the trajectory is actually a broken line, with the free path of the electron intervening between the various deflections.

In many actual practical cases the resultant of this series of successive deflections must be known.

A theory on this has been developed by Molière[16] and by Snyder and Scott[17], both of which give similar results. The simplest way of presenting the results is to use the form adopted by the last-mentioned workers. We shall consider a particle with unit charge (not necessarily an electron) undergoing displacement on an axis Oz of a system of rectangular co-ordinates $Oxyz$, and passing through a foil of thickness δ placed on the plane xOy. On passing out of the foil, the particle is travelling in a direction which is not Oz, and when projected upon the plane xOz it makes an angle η with Oz. The theory allows the derivation of an expression for the probability $\phi(\eta)\mathrm{d}\eta$ that the incident particle, after passing through the thickness δ of the medium composed of atoms of nuclear charge Ze, shall have a deflection of direction lying between η and $\eta + \mathrm{d}\eta$.

In order to express the results in a convenient way, it is best to express the quantities involved in appropriate units. For the angle η we choose as our unit the value η_0 given by

$$\eta_0 = \frac{Z^{\frac{1}{3}}}{137} \cdot \frac{mc}{p},$$

in which m is the electronic mass, p the quantity of movement of the incident particle, and η_0 is expressed in radians.

As our unit for thickness of material we take the length λ given by

$$\frac{1}{\lambda} = \frac{4\pi r^2}{\alpha^2} Z^{\frac{4}{3}} N \left(\frac{p}{\mu c}\right)^2 \left(\frac{W}{T}\right)^2 = 1\cdot 87 \times 10^{-20} Z^{\frac{4}{3}} N \left(\frac{p}{\mu c}\right)^2 \left(\frac{W}{T}\right)^2,$$

in which α is $\frac{1}{137}$, r is $e^2/mc^2 = 2\cdot 82 \times 10^{-13}$ cm. or the classical radius of the electron, N is the number of atoms per c.c., μ, W and T are respectively the rest mass, total energy and the kinetic energy of the incident particle, and λ is in cm.

If the thickness is in terms of mass per unit area, M, the unit becomes λd, where d is the specific mass of the medium, and

$$\frac{1}{\lambda d} = 1\cdot 87 \times 10^{-20} Z^{\frac{4}{3}} \frac{\mathbf{N}}{A} \left(\frac{p}{\mu c}\right)^2 \left(\frac{W}{T}\right)^2 = 11\cdot 25 \times 10^3 . \frac{Z^{\frac{4}{3}}}{A} \left(\frac{p}{\mu c}\right)^2 \left(\frac{W}{T}\right)^2$$

in which $\mathbf{N}$ is the Avogadro number, and A the atomic mass of the medium considered.

If t and γ represent respectively the thickness and the angle measured in the chosen units, then

$$t = \frac{\delta}{\lambda} = \frac{M}{d\lambda} \qquad \gamma = \frac{\eta}{\eta_0}$$

and the probability law referring to γ takes the form which depends only on t and γ, the characteristics of the medium and the incident particle having now vanished.

Let $\phi(\gamma, t)\mathrm{d}\gamma$ be the probability for deflection between γ and $\gamma + \mathrm{d}\gamma$ during traverse of the thickness t of the medium. Then we have

$$\phi(\gamma, t)\mathrm{d}\gamma = f\left(\frac{\gamma}{t^{\frac{1}{2}}}\right) \frac{\mathrm{d}\gamma}{t^{\frac{1}{2}}}$$

and the function f varies little as t varies within wide limits, indicating that the probability for deflection is, to a first approximation, conditioned by the combination $\gamma/t^{\frac{1}{2}}$, and we may interpret this as meaning that the deflection increases proportionally with the square root of the thickness, all other conditions being equal. Figs. 71 and 72, due to Snyder and Scott, show the function f for three values of thickness, these being selected over a wide range, namely, $t = 100$, 1500 and 84000.

The validity of these results is limited to the case where the total deflection angle is smaller than 1 radian, and this means when the particles are comparatively fast-moving and the thicknesses traversed are quite small. Under these conditions the greatest deflections observed correspond essentially to nuclear impacts produced once

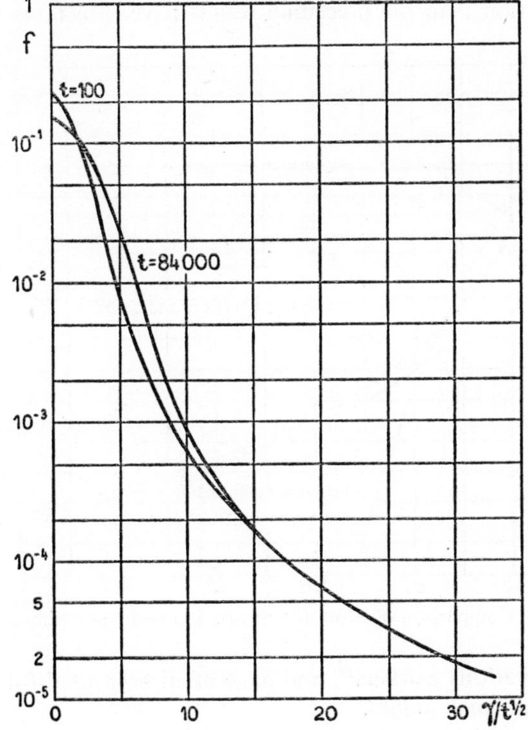

FIG. 71.—Multiple diffusion law, after Snyder and Scott.

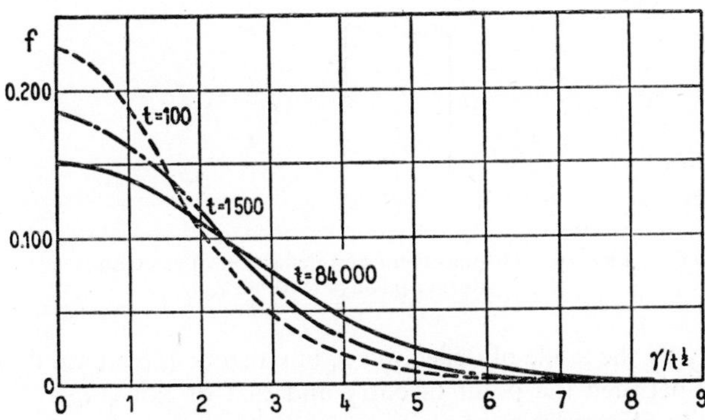

FIG. 72.—Multiple diffusion law, after Snyder and Scott.

during the course of the trajectory, and as a result, the probability law tends asymptotically towards the law which is valid for a single impact, i.e. the Rutherford law. Fig. 73 shows, for the case when t is 100, the law of Snyder and Scott, and also that of Rutherford.

Formulæ of the gaussian type correspond to a less satisfactory approximation than the preceding results have shown, as has been

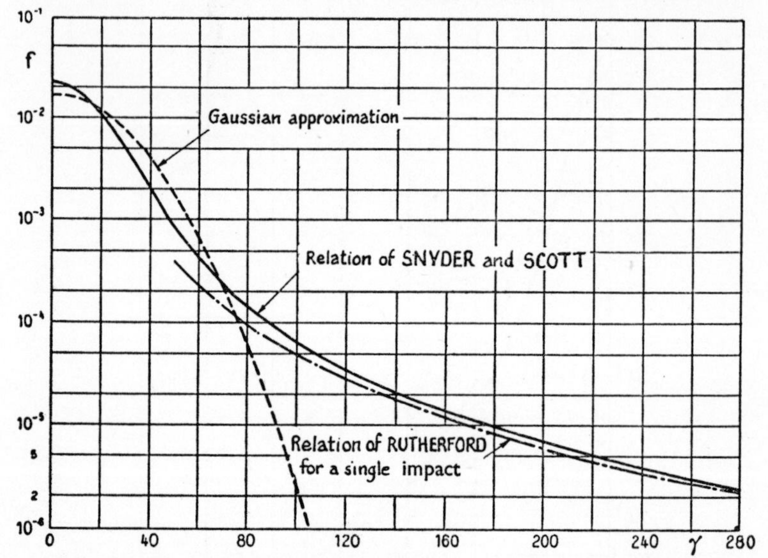

FIG. 73.—Comparison of Scott and Snyder law with approximate laws.

shown by various workers[18], and have often been used for multiple deflection at small angles.

If we project upon the plane xOz the trajectory of the particle which has traversed a thickness δ of the foil, this is characterized,

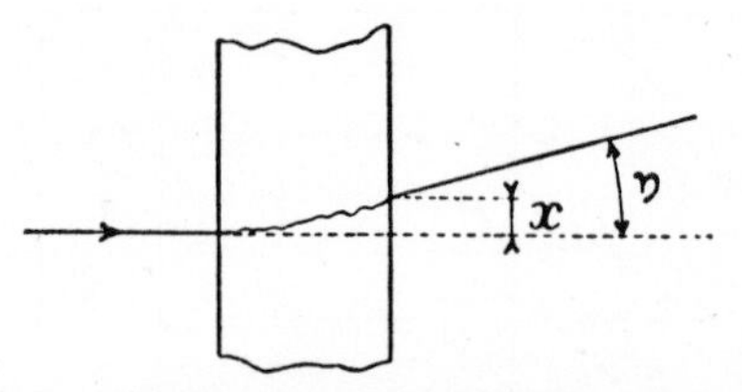

FIG. 74.—Displacement and deflection of electrons during passage through foil.

not only by the angle of deflection η, but also by the lateral displacement x between the point of entry and that of exit (Fig. 74). The probability law relating these two quantities is given by

$$\phi(x, \eta, \delta) = \frac{k\sqrt{3}}{2\pi\delta^2} \exp\left\{-\frac{k}{\delta}\left[\eta^2 - \frac{3\eta x}{\delta} + \frac{3x^2}{\delta^2}\right]\right\},$$

where k is the length defined by the expression

$$\frac{1}{k} = 2\pi r^2 \left(\frac{mc}{p}\right)^2 \frac{1}{\beta^2} \cdot Z^2 N \log \frac{150}{Z^{\frac{1}{3}}} \cdot \frac{p}{mc}$$

when k is expressed in cm.

By integration with respect to η, we find that we have the law relating to x only, and this is

$$\phi(x, \delta) = \left(\frac{3k}{4\pi\delta^3}\right)^{\frac{3}{2}} \exp\left(-\frac{3kx^2}{4\delta^3}\right),$$

and integration with respect to x gives us the law for η only,

$$\phi(\eta, \delta) = \left(\frac{k}{4\pi\delta}\right)^{\frac{1}{2}} \exp\left(-\frac{k\eta^2}{4\delta}\right).$$

From this last formula, it is seen that the mean square of η is

$$\overline{\eta^2} = \frac{2\delta}{k}.$$

If Φ is the angle of deflection in space and not on the projection, we have

$$\overline{\Phi^2} = 2\overline{\eta^2} \qquad \text{or} \qquad \overline{\Phi^2} = \frac{4\delta}{k}$$

and under these conditions we may say that $4/k$ is the mean square deflection per unit length of the thickness traversed.

On Fig. 73, we find, as did Snyder and Scott, the gaussian approximation corresponding to the formula preceding; this is rather more correct, but cannot be simply expressed by a formula.

Reverting back to the definition of k, we see that $\overline{\eta^2}$ is proportional to $1/p^2\beta^2$, and as result, the measure of the multiple deflection is susceptible to interpretation in terms of the product of the quantity of movement of the particle and the speed of this. This property is often utilized by physicists, who make use of the measurement of the multiple deflection along the trajectories of rapid particles recorded in photographic emulsions, in order to arrive at the quantity $p\beta$.

REFERENCES

1. MÖLLER, C. (1932), *Ann. Phys. Lpz.*, **14,** 531.
2. BETHE, H. (1933), *Handbuch der Physik*, **24/1,** 515.
3. WILLIAMS, E. J. (1929), *Proc. Roy. Soc.* A, **125,** 445.
4. LANDAU, L. (1944), *Sechenov. J. Physiol.*, **8,** 201.
5. STERNHEIMER, R. M. (1953), *Phys. Rev.*, **91,** 256; (1952), **88,** 855.
6. GOLDWASSER, E. L., MILLS, F. E., and HANSON, A. O. (1952), *Phys. Rev.*, **88,** 1137.

7. Bethe, H. A., and Heitler, W. (1934), *Proc. Roy. Soc.* A, **146**, 83.
8. Rossi, B. B., and Greisen, K. I. (1941), *Rev. Mod. Phys.*, **13**, 240.
9. Bethe, H. A., and Ashkin, J., 'Passage of Radiations through Matter', p. 266 of *Experimental Nuclear Physics*, vol. 1 (E. Segré, editor).
10. Mott, N. F. (1929), *Proc. Roy. Soc.* A, **124**, 425.
11. McKinley, W. A., and Feshbach, H. (1948), *Phys. Rev.*, **74**, 1759.
12. Feshbach, H. (1953), *Phys. Rev.*, **92**, 988.
13. Molière, G. (1948), *Z. Naturf.*, **3A**, 78.
14. Hofstadter, H., Fechter, H. R., and McIntyre, J. A. (1953), *Phys. Rev.*, **92**, 978.
15. Schiff, L. I. (1953), *Phys. Rev.*, **92**, 988.
16. Molière, G. (1948), *Z. Naturf.*, **3A**, 78.
17. Snyder, H. S., and Scott, W. T. (1949), *Phys. Rev.*, **76**, 220.
18. E.g. Scott, W. T. (1949), *Phys. Rev.*, **76**, 220.

Chapter 11

ELECTRONS: EXPERIMENTAL ASPECTS

(1) General

In the preceding chapter have been presented a number of theoretical studies of various aspects of the behaviour of electrons during their passage through matter. Many experiments have been carried out with the object of testing the validity of results. Such experiments often involve serious difficulties, as it is rarely possible to arrange conditions so that the phenomena under investigation can be dealt with in isolation, and under conditions for which the theory has been constructed. There are usually many phenomena occurring simultaneously and it is often difficult to decide in the observed effects what contributions are made by each. For example, if we seek to measure the energy loss from electrons during their passage through a thin foil, we must take notice of the energy loss by ionization and by excitation, and the loss by Bremsstrahlung, and also of the fact that as a result of deviation during passage through the foil, the actual track of the electron is rather greater than the thickness of the foil. The elucidation of elementary phenomena is, from the experimental point of view, much more difficult to carry out than in the case of atomic particles.

Fortunately, the basis on which the theory has been developed is quite sound; the uncertainties in the results arise from the difficulty of making calculations with approximations, and these must be evaluated. In spite of such experimental difficulties, the situation is fairly satisfactory.

(2) Deceleration by Ionization and Excitation

It is necessary to test the validity of the distribution of energy losses given by Landau.

The principle of measurement is quite simple. First of all a parallel beam of electrons, all of one energy, is obtained by using a magnetic spectrograph in order to separate electrons of energy close to a value T from the beam leaving an accelerator, or alternatively a radio-element may be used as the source. The beam so selected is directed perpendicularly on to a thin foil of the material to be examined, the emergent beam from the foil being then analysed for energy distribution by means of a second magnetic spectrograph. As typical experiments may be quoted those of Chen and Warshaw[1] carried out with electrons selected from the specta of various radio-elements between 87 kev and 1 Mev, their deceleration being studied during their passage through different metals. These workers concentrated their attention upon the most probable energy loss, while restricting themselves to ascertaining that the distribution due to Landau was compatible with their results; the difficulties involved in the resolving power of their magnetic spectrograph would allow no further decisions. Except for beryllium and carbon, experiments have confirmed the value of the Landau formula in forecasting the most probable energy losses.

At higher energies measurements have been carried out by Goldwasser, Mills and Hanson[2], making use of electrons from the betatron, with energies of 9·6 and 15·7 Mev. For light media, these workers have found results in satisfactory agreement with the Landau theory (provided the density correction has been applied) regarding the value of the theory, and the distribution of energy losses. With heavy elements, experimental results are complicated by the intervention of the contribution due to Bremsstrahlung and by the necessity to take into account the elongation of the trajectory in the foil. When all effects are considered, the most probable energy loss is somewhat smaller than the calculated loss, but the Landau curve corrected for these effects explains the loss distribution in a satisfactory way. In the case of copper, if the various corrections[3] are included, the agreement is satisfactory.

(3) Ionization by Electrons

(a) *Ionization chamber method*

In this method, a beam of electrons, of fixed energy and constant intensity, is sent into an ionization chamber of effective length l. The ionization current is a measure of the number of ion-pairs I created per unit time along the length l of the beam in the gas in the chamber. If we know the number N of electrons penetrating the chamber in unit time, we can deduce the number of ion-pairs I/N created per electron along the length l. In order to measure N we can replace the ionization chamber by a Faraday cage and determine the charge C which it collects per second. Then $N = C/e$.

Such measurements have been carried out, in particular by W. Wilson[4] and S. Bloch[5], who found that the mean number of ion-pairs formed per cm. in air under normal conditions of temperature and pressure, as a function of electron energy, was as follows:

T kev:	60	100	150	200	315	380	460
	214	155	128	94	74	68	61

T kev:	600	770	1000	1200	1340	1460
	56	55	53	50	47	46

This variation shows a behaviour similar to the decelerating power by ionization and excitation within the energy region studied. It shows clearly the increase in ionizing power as the energy decreases.

This type of method is particularly applicable to electrons of low energy for which the ionizing power is high. It has been used in particular by Tate and Smith[6] for measuring the ionization by electrons of kinetic energy below 750 ev.

(b) *Wilson cloud chamber method*

The tracking of ions by droplets in the atmosphere of a Wilson cloud chamber enables us to count ions easily, at least at energies which are not too low, when the droplets are reasonably separated. The region of application of this method is thus essentially to electrons with energies around those for minimum ionization.

The inconvenience of the method lies in the fact that it measures ionization in a complex medium, containing at least a vapour and a gas. The results so obtained are valid for that medium, but we must be cautious in any attempt to transfer such results to the pure gases comprising the mixture. We have already seen, in connection with the work of Jesse and Sadauskis on ionization by α-particles, how minute traces of impurities can often introduce errors by virtue of energy transfer phenomena.

The most recent measurements by this method are those of Frost and Nielsen[7], who obtained the following results for the specific ionization by electrons at minimum ionization:

Air	H_2	He	A	
$46 \cdot 1 \pm 2 \cdot 2$	$6 \cdot 48 \pm 0 \cdot 34$	$8 \cdot 13 \pm 0 \cdot 51$	$53 \cdot 1 \pm 2 \cdot 8$	ion-pairs per cm. at N.T.P.

corresponding to energy losses per ion-pair created:

$31 \cdot 2 \pm 1 \cdot 5$	$37 \cdot 2 \pm 2 \cdot 0$	$26 \cdot 0 \pm 1 \cdot 6$	$27 \cdot 9 \pm 1 \cdot 5$	ev.

In the case of air, and more especially of helium, these values differ from those obtained by Jesse and Sadauskis for α-particles, but this is not considered as significant, because of the difficulties already mentioned.

(c) *Method using coincidence counters*

If along the path of an electron the average number of ion-pairs formed per unit length is k, and these are randomly distributed, the probability that there is, within an element dl of the trajectory, one pair of ions formed, is $k\,dl$. Probability considerations show that under these conditions, for an element of trajectory l, the probability that no ion-pairs will be formed is e^{-kl}.

This probability law is used in measuring k. Let us consider a Geiger counter of diameter l, traversed by an electron of specific ionization k. If the electron creates no ion-pairs in the counter, the latter gives no discharge response, but if one or more ion-pairs are formed, discharge occurs. If now the counter is crossed by a large number of electrons N, and if n of these do not cause discharge, then

$$\frac{n}{N} = e^{-kl} \quad \text{or} \quad k = \frac{1}{l}\log\frac{N}{n}\cdot$$

Thus, determination of k gives the ratio N/n. In order to achieve this, we use Geiger counters in coincidence, in the following way for example. In Fig. 75 are shown three counters, C_1, C_2, C_3, side by

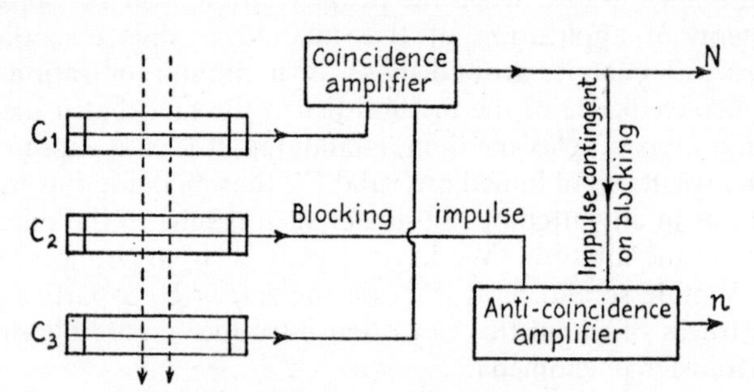

FIG. 75.—Principle of set-up for measuring electron ionization by means of Geiger counters.

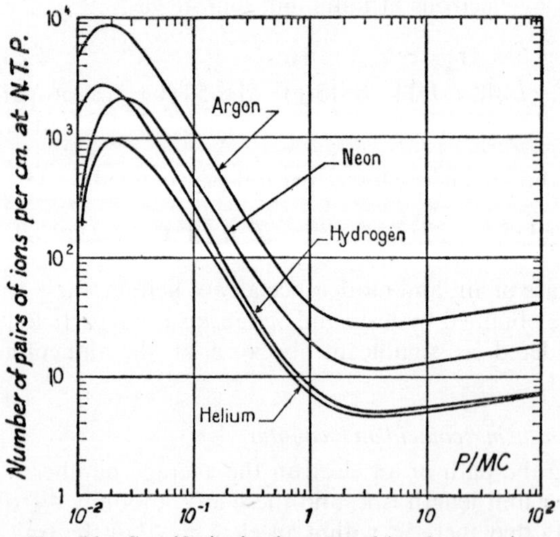

FIG. 76.—Specific ionization caused by electrons in various gases.

side and traversed by the same beam of electrons all of given energy. Consider among these electrons only those which discharge at least C_1 and C_3, and neglect those which have not discharged the intermediate counter C_2. Let N be this number during the time T of the measurement. This will be measured by the required number of coincidences between counters C_1 and C_3. Each of these electrons must also have passed through counter C_2, though not necessarily discharging it. In order to find n, it is necessary to bring to an anti-coincident amplifier the impulses from the C_1C_3 coincidences, and those from C_2, these last exerting a blocking action. The apparatus will only register the n C_1C_3 coincidences which are not accompanied by discharge of C_2. From measurements of N and n we can deduce the value of k for the gas used in filling the counter at a given pressure. The figure can then easily be transferred to conditions of normal temperature and pressure.

The most recent use of this method is by McClure[8], who obtained results for hydrogen, helium, neon and argon. Fig. 76, due to this author, gives the results obtained, and it is seen that in the region studied the variation in specific ionization is very close to that in decelerating power.

The values obtained at minimum ionization are, especially in the case of helium and argon, very different from those obtained by the Wilson chamber method, indicating the difficulty of interpretation of results in that method.

(d) *Method of photographic emulsions*

A charged particle moving in a photographic emulsion gives rise to ionization in the granules of AgBr which it traverses. When a granule receives more than a certain minimum number of ion-pairs, it can be developed, and gives rise to a grain of Ag by the action of the developer. The trajectory of a charged particle thus manifests itself as a line of silver grains which can be examined under the microscope. For a given type of emulsion and a given developing schedule, the number of Ag grains per unit length of trajectory is higher as the specific ionization increases and the two are really proportional. It is almost certainly true only for weak specific ionizations, in the region of the minimum, but there exists between them a reciprocal relationship such that the density of the grains can be considered as a function of the specific ionization even though the limits of the proportionality are not always clearly defined.

Fig. 77, due to Stiller and Shapiro[9], shows how the grain density varies with the ratio between the energy W and the rest mass of the particle, as this ratio rises to the value 3000. The measurements were carried out with the particles of cosmic rays, and thus include protons as well as electrons and mesons, though this is unimportant, since all the particles are singly charged, and obey the same law provided the energies are put as ratios of the rest mass. On the graph appears the curve calculated from Bethe's theory after application of Sternheimer's density correction. The agreement is seen to be satisfactory, and in particular, the ionization does not increase indefinitely but tends towards a limiting value as the energy increases.

In order to become applicable to this type of measurement, the Bethe theory must be slightly modified. In the Bethe theory it is supposed that, during ionization, the energy imparted to an electron can reach half that of the original electron; but when a great proportion of the incident energy is transferred, the particle acquiring the energy becomes itself capable of ionizing, and gives rise to a secondary observable trajectory. In such a case, as in the experiment performed by means of the Wilson cloud chamber, one takes into account only the ions created in the primary trajectory.

We may designate by T_0 the energy starting from which the secondary trajectory becomes observable, and consider only the impacts corresponding to an energy transfer smaller than T_0, in place of $T/2$.

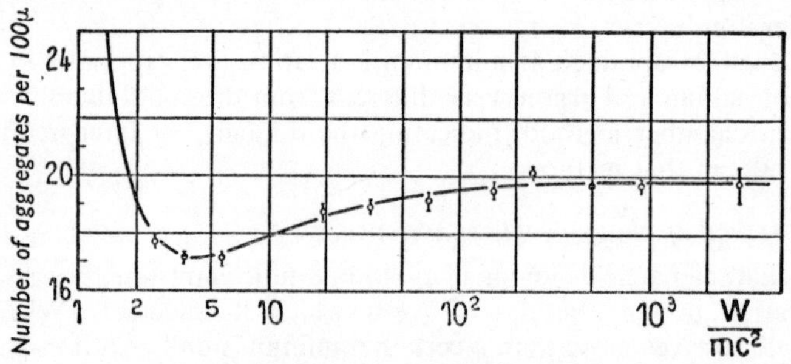

FIG. 77.—Grain density along a path in a photographic emulsion as a function of particle energy.

(4) Electronic Deflection of Electrons

Many experiments have been carried out with a view to studying the deflection of electrons—electronic, nuclear, and multiple deflection.

Electronic deflection is distinguished experimentally from nuclear deflection only when the projected electron receives sufficient energy to have an observable trajectory, which signifies, at least when the incident electrons are not highly energetic, that the angles of deflection and projection are not very small. One method of studying this type of deflection is the Wilson cloud chamber placed in a magnetic field so that one can deduce the energies of the particles from the curvature of the trajectories. By this means, measurements have been made for many years. In 1932, Champion studied in this way electronic deflection in nitrogen of β-rays of energies between 400 and 800 kev. Mention may be made also of the work of Groetzinger and his co-workers[10] in the energy region 50 kev to 1·7 Mev. The disadvantage of the method is that the rarity of the phenomenon leads to few data, even when larger numbers of photographs are taken, and so the results lack precision. Apart from this they agree with Möller's theory.

Another method of experimental study, which supplies plenty of statistics, is to record the diffusion by discharging a pair of coincidence counters by means of the moving ions after an impact. As shown in Fig. 78, a narrow beam of monokinetic electrons is allowed to impinge upon a thin foil beyond which is placed a counter C_1 which receives the electrons leaving the foil at angle ϕ to the original direction. If the deflection is due to electronic diffusion, the angle θ at which the other electron leaves the foil is easily calculated by means of the conservation relationships, and this enables one to arrange a second counter C_2 so that the second electron can be received. If $d\Omega_1$ is the solid angle at which C_1 has to be placed, with respect to the point of impact of the incident beam, we can calculate the minimum angle $d\Omega_2$ at which C_2 has to be placed in order to

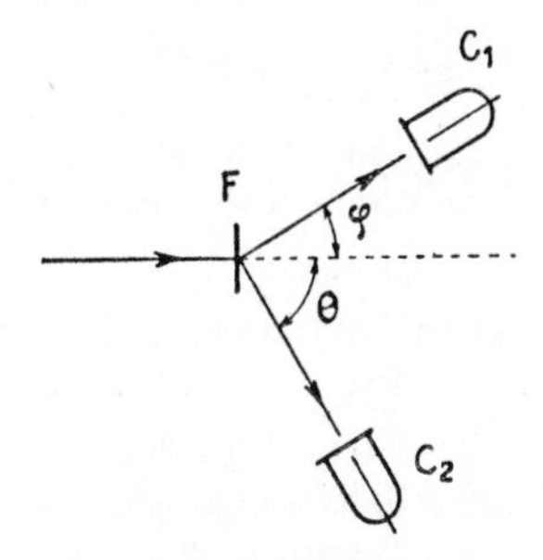

FIG. 78.—Apparatus for measuring electronic deflection of electrons.

trap each corresponding electron, if the diffusion is truly electronic. From the measure of the intensity of the incident beam and of the number of coincidences in C_1 and C_2, we can find the effective cross-section for electronic diffusion with the solid angle $d\Omega_1$, of the angle ϕ. Such measurements have been made by Page[11] between 0·6 and 1·7 Mev with thin foils of beryllium and collodion, while Barber and his co-workers[12] have done similar work with 6·1-Mev electrons and foils of beryllium. The use of light materials in these experiments was necessary in order to avoid nuclear diffusion and multiple diffusion. Results were in agreement with the Möller theory.

A third experimental method was used by Scott and his collaborators[13], using 15·7-Mev electrons. Electronic diffusion was recognized by measuring the energy of the diffused electrons. A narrow beam of monokinetic electrons (Fig. 79) was allowed to fall upon a thin foil, the diffusing electrons being received with an angle ϕ in the magnetic spectrometer S, in which two energy groups were observed, one group having the same energy as the undeviated electrons, and another group with lower energy. The first group consisted of electrons which had suffered nuclear diffusion, the second group those suffering electronic diffusion. The proportion of electrons in the second group is a measure of the effective cross-section for electronic diffusion. Once again the Möller formula was found to agree very well with experimental results.

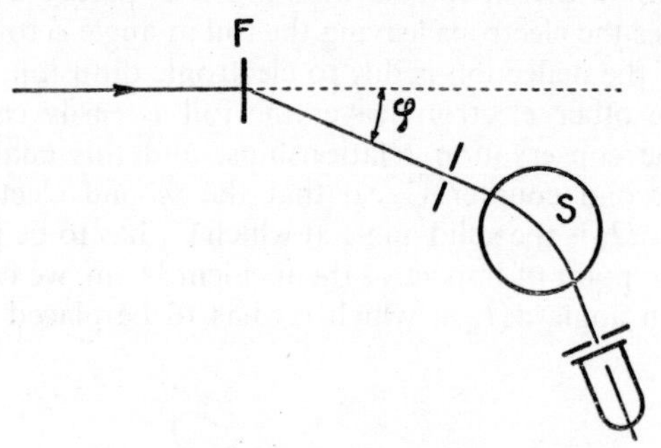

FIG. 79.—Apparatus for measuring electronic deflection of electrons.

(5) NUCLEAR DIFFUSION OF ELECTRONS

The diffusion by the nuclei of Be, Al, Cu, Ag, Pt and Au, of electrons of energies 1·27 to 2·27 Mev, accelerated in a Van de Graaff machine, has been studied between angles of 20° and 60° by the physicists at Massachusetts Institute of Technology[14]. The method, illustrated in Fig. 80, involves sending the beam of electrons from the accelerator onto a thin metal foil F, which is traversed before the beam is received in a detector D_1, where the intensity is measured. Another detector, D_2, placed laterally, receives the deflected beam

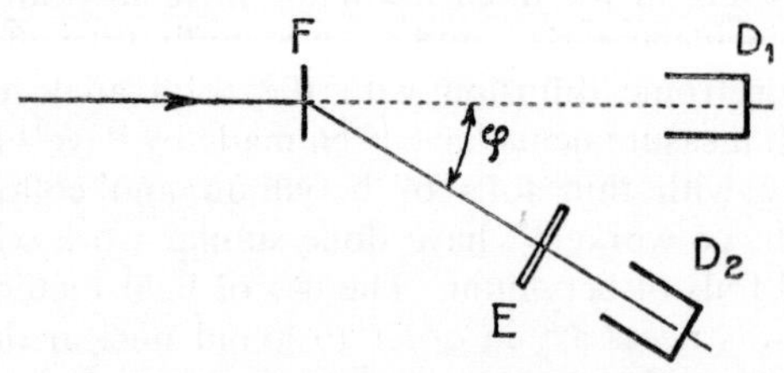

FIG. 80.—Apparatus for measuring nuclear deflection of electrons.

within the angle ϕ which can vary from 20° to 60°. In order to avoid receiving in D_2 the electrons from the electronic diffusion or from inelastic nuclear diffusion, the energy of which would be smaller than that of the electrons deflected by elastic nuclear diffusion, we interpose on the trajectory an absorber E of sufficient thickness to stop the weaker group of particles. Results were in good agreement with the theories of Mott, McKinley and Feshbach.

The third method mentioned for electronic diffusion can be applied to the study of nuclear diffusion, and has been used[15] for electrons of 15·7 Mev. Only the light elements have shown good agreement with Mott's formula. In the case of other elements, the effective cross-section for diffusion as experimentally determined is larger than that calculated, especially at large angles, the correction factor being as large as 2·7 in the case of gold at 150°.

This divergence from theory is probably due to the necessity, already mentioned, of considering the nuclear charge as non-point when dealing with high energy electrons. There is, in fact, a great improvement in the agreement between the experimental results at 157 Mev and theoretical forecast, if the idea of a point charge is replaced by a uniform distribution of charge over the volume of the nucleus.

(6) Multiple Deflection of Electrons

Experiments on this have been very few, but mention must be made of the work of a group of Soviet physicists[16] and of the researches of Hanson and his co-workers[17]. The first group worked with 2·25-Mev electrons and a wide range of materials, the second with 15·7-Mev electrons with Be and Au as the deflecting substances. The results for the angular distribution of electrons after traversing the various materials agreed well with theory.

(7) Experimental Study of Bremsstrahlung

Experimental results concerned with Bremsstrahlung have been relatively few, partly as a result of the experimental difficulties, which were not easy to surmount until the technical developments of the last few years.

Since the development of the use of betatrons for the production of high energy X-rays by means of braking action, a number of measurements have been made, but they refer mainly to very high energy electrons and are even now subject to experimental error. We shall examine a few of these results quite briefly, taking them in order of increasing energies.

Goodrich and his co-workers[18] have studied the Bremsstrahlung produced by the β-rays from P-32 (maximum energy 1·7 Mev) stopped by copper. The energy spectrum of these photons was determined by means of a spectrometer fitted with a sodium iodide crystal. Within 10 per cent, the spectrum was that predicted by the Bethe-Heitler theory for photons between 50 and 1100 kev. But the complexity of the experimental conditions, especially the use of a continuous spectrum of electrons and of a thick target, makes it difficult fully to evaluate the results.

Buechner and his collaborators[19] used monokinetic electrons of energy between 1250 and 2350 kev from a Van de Graaff generator.

By means of an ionization chamber they measured the quantity of X-rays (*see* Chapter 12 for a definition of this) emitted in various directions when the electrons struck a thick target. Because of the use of a thick target, and more especially as a result of diffusion of electrons within such a target, it is difficult to align the results with the Bethe-Heitler theory. Nevertheless, these physicists have shown that, for the various energies of the electrons which they employed, the total intensity of radiation obtained by summation over all directions of emission is proportional to Z of the target, a result which can readily be forecast by the Bethe-Heitler theory, which thus receives partial confirmation. Further, they have shown that in the case of a gold target, and with 2·35-Mev electrons, 7·4 per cent of the energy of the incident electrons is emitted in the form of X-rays, whereas the theory indicates 8·3 per cent. Considering the experimental difficulties, this agreement may be considered very good.

Lanzl and Hanson[20] studied the rays produced by 17-Mev electrons falling upon relatively thin targets of various materials. They used as detector a copper foil of which the activation was measured, this being the result of the (γ, n) reaction. The threshold for this reaction is at 10·9 Mev, so that only the more energetic portion of the spectrum is recorded. Remembering that the screening effect necessitates only minute corrections in the upper part of the spectrum, the observed activation must be proportional to NZ^2, N being the number of atoms per c.c. of the target and Z its atomic number. The results indicate that, to within 1 per cent, the proportionality is to $N(Z^2+0{\cdot}75Z)$, or at least for Be, Al, Cu, Ag and Au.

The term $0{\cdot}75Z$ is easily understood, for it corresponds to the Bremsstrahlung produced in the field of the electrons in the target, and agrees with theoretical forecasts that it should be somewhat smaller than that produced in the field of a proton.

Measurements, by the same workers, of the effective section of radiation, by measuring with an ionization chamber the total radiated intensity, seem to show, at least in the case of gold, a value 10 per cent lower than the theoretical.

The angular distribution of the radiation agrees with theory if we take into account the diffusion of the electrons in the target.

Koch and Carter[21] have studied the radiation from a thin target of platinum struck by a beam of 19·5-Mev electrons from a betatron. The photons emitted in the axis of the beam of electrons, carefully collimated by lead screens, pass through the Wilson cloud chamber in the gas of which the ion-pairs are formed. The chamber is placed in a magnetic field, and from the curvature of the trajectories the energy of the pair is deduced, and hence that of the photon. Measurement of the energy distribution of the pairs enables one to deduce that of the corresponding photons if one knows the law giving the relation between the creation of ion-pairs in the chamber gas and the energy.

This method, though excellent in principle, suffers from the inconvenience which accompanies most measurements of strong effective sections in the Wilson chamber, i.e. the number of phenomena is very limited, and hence the precision of the results is correspondingly low. Further, it has to be assumed, in the absence of more exact information, that the theoretical law giving the effective section for pair formation is exact. With these reservations, it appears that the spectrum is a little richer in photons of mean average (above 10 Mev) than would be expected from the Bethe-Heitler theory.

Curtis[22] studied inelastic collision of electrons of 60-Mev energy during their passage through thin foils of lead placed in a Wilson chamber placed in a magnetic field such that the energies of the electrons could be ascertained before and after the traverse. Each time that this is accompanied by a great energy loss, this latter is distributed with emission of a braking photon with energy equal to that lost. If there were no difficulties due to the scarcity of statistical results, this method would allow one to measure the absolute value of effective cross-sections with comparative ease.

It is shown that the spectrum of photons emitted between 42 and 60 Mev was of the form forecast by theory, but the corresponding effective cross-sections were lower than the theoretical values to the extent of about 7 per cent.

The same method has been used by Fisher[23] for a study of Bremsstrahlung in gold, from positive and negative electrons of 247-Mev energy. The results were the same for both types of particles, and it was noticed that, in the upper part of the spectrum, the effective cross-section was about 9 per cent lower than the theoretical value.

Dewire and Beach[24], using a pair-spectrometer, studied braking photons due to electrons of 312-Mev energy striking a thin target of tungsten. The form of the spectrum agreed with theory, but the absolute value of the cross-sections was not determined.

From all these results we may conclude that there is no serious lack of agreement between theoretical and experimental results, but at high energies the experimental values are slightly lower than the theoretically forecast ones.

(8) Transmission of Electrons across Thin Metal Foils

Besides the problems which have just been discussed and which deal more or less directly with the theory of the phenomena induced by the passage of electrons through matter, a certain number of problems of a practical nature involve the simultaneous occurrence of several phenomena and are thus not amenable to a simple treatment by a theoretical approach, and so we must have recourse to experimental results.

One of these problems is that of transmission across a thin material foil. If a monokinetic beam of electrons strikes normally such a foil, a fraction t of the electrons of the beam issues from the other face, having undergone a certain degree of slowing down; another fraction a is completely stopped in the foil, while a third fraction r is dispersed backwards, and emerges from the entry-face by simple or multiple diffusion.

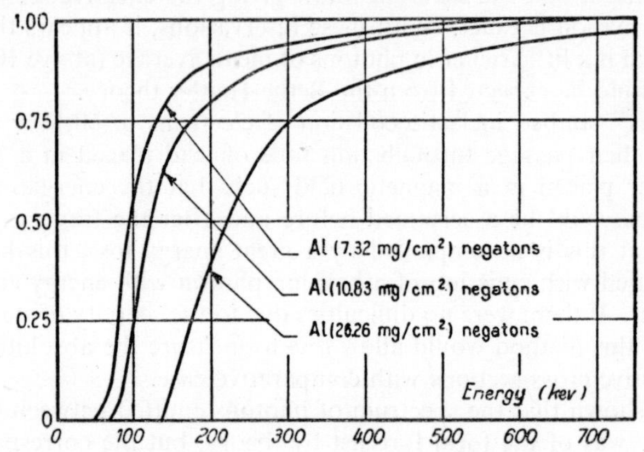

FIG. 81.—Electron transmission through thin aluminium foils.

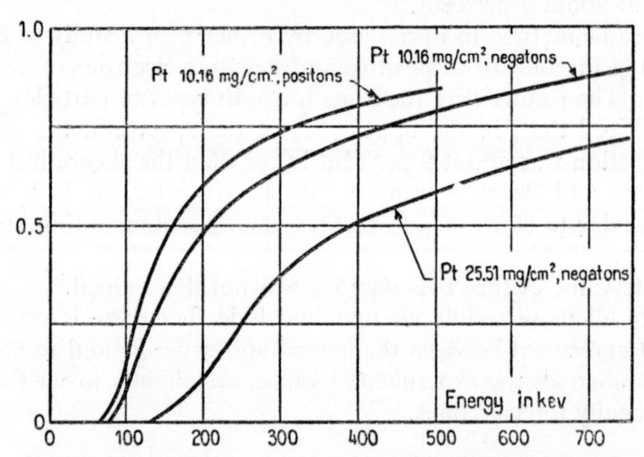

FIG. 82.—Electron transmission through thin platinum foils.

A knowledge of these three fractions as a function of the nature and the thickness of the foils on the one hand, and of the energy of the incident electrons on the other, is necessary for a satisfactory explanation of the experiments in which the electrons are in motion.

Some measurements were made around 1923 by Schonland[25] on 10–80-kev electrons, and since that time other workers have carried out similar experiments, usually restricted to the transmitted fraction. Among the most recent may be mentioned those of Chang and

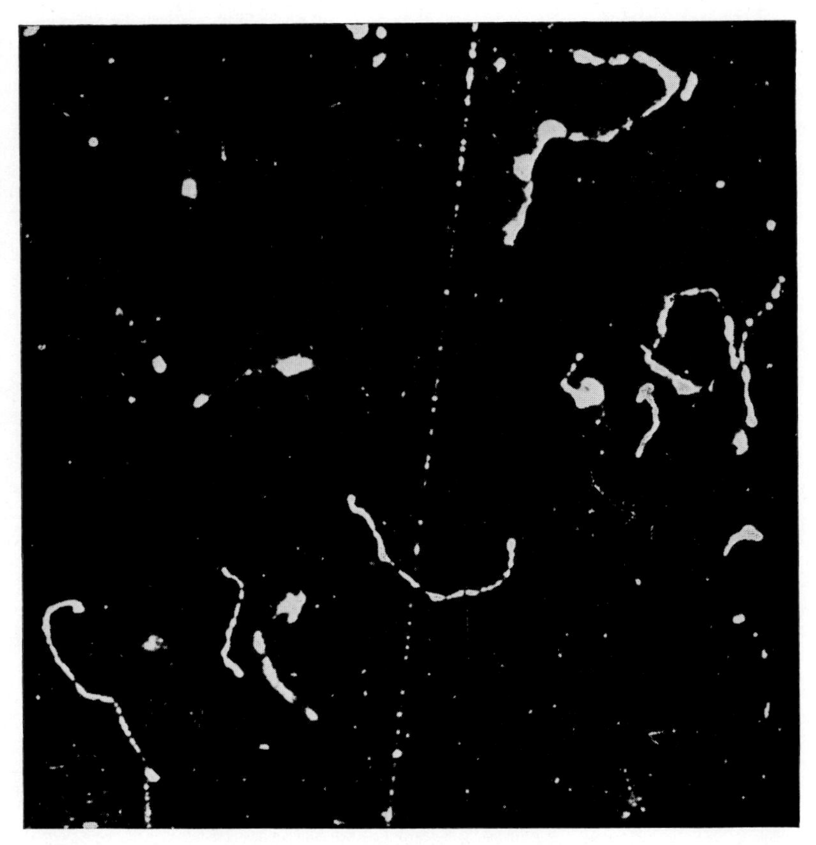

FIG. 83.—Tracks of fast electrons (rectilinear and with little ionization) and of slow electrons (sinuous and strongly ionizing) photographed in the Wilson cloud chamber.

his co-workers[26], who studied foils of aluminium and platinum. The results of these measurements are collected together in Figs. 81 and 82.

It will be noted that in the case of platinum, the transmission of the positons is greater than that of negatons, by virtue of the fact that the diffusion of the first is smaller than that of the second. Equally, at equal mass per unit area the transmission in aluminium is larger than in platinum even though the energy at which zero transmission commences is the same for both media. This is due to the diffusion being greater in platinum than in aluminium.

(9) The Path of Electrons

The notion of path is less clearly marked with electrons than with heavier particles because of the considerable variations in individual behaviour between two electrons even under the same initial conditions. In a region where the only cause of deceleration is the ionization and excitation of atoms and molecules of the medium, conditions are similar to those for heavy particles, and it may be expected that the mean path followed by an electron will be clearly defined and that variations from such a path will be small. But this assumes that consideration is taken only of relatively low energies (well below the critical energy) such that braking action, an important cause of dispersion, is negligible. But at low energies the diffusion becomes important and the path adopted by each electron is a tortuous one which is generally difficult to determine with precision.

Hardly any method apart from the Wilson chamber is able to record the trajectory (see Fig. 83), and it is even then difficult to measure the corrected length of the trajectory. Such measurements have been made by Tsien and co-workers[27], who have compared values found in air with those obtained by integrating the Bethe equation at low energies, when a fair agreement was obtained.

In practice the complications are such that one is obliged to give up the idea of trying to define the path as the actual track followed by the electron, and one has to find some empirical relationship. Absorption methods give us such a possibility. If we measure, as a function of the foil thickness, the transmitted portion of a beam of monokinetic electrons of not too high energy (below a few Mev), we get a curve which has the shape shown in Fig. 84. This shows a rectilinear portion which can be prolonged so that it cuts the abscissa axis, and the intersection may be used to define the path of the electrons of the given energy in the medium in question.

The absorption has often been determined in the case of electron beams formed by the spectra of radioactive elements, and which are not monokinetic.

The absorption curve is the sum of the elementary absorption curves for each of the monokinetic components into which the spectrum may be broken up. Further, for reasons of intensity, it is not often possible to restrict the bundle of rays so that they will become parallel. The general trend of the absorption curves obtained is shown in Fig. 85.

It may be stated here that it is usual to represent intensities by logarithmic co-ordinates, and the curve ends in a rectilinear portion

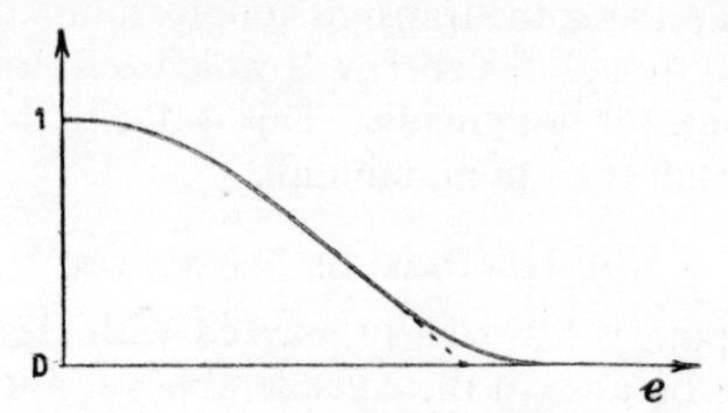

FIG. 84.—Absorption curve for a mono-kinetic beam of electrons.

of feeble slope, indicating an exponential absorption. This is frequently the case where the source of β-rays also emits γ-rays to which the apparatus measuring the β-rays is also sensitive (a G.M. tube, for example). Under such conditions the definition of the track becomes even more difficult.

We might try to define a point P where the absorption curve joins that corresponding only to the γ-rays. But the tangential junction

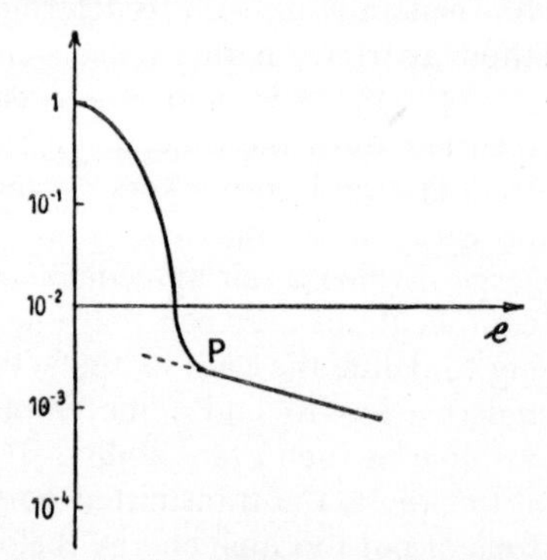

FIG. 85.—Absorption curve for β-rays.

will not allow very precise definition of such a point. Various workers have proposed different methods for increasing precision, and this matter is dealt with in a summary work by Katz and Penfold[28]. The methods consist in the application of a technique which allows one to deduce the value of the track by an extrapolation of the initial part of the curve where the effect of the γ-rays is negligible. A criterion of validity, apparently satisfactory in the case of the various methods proposed, is that the track obtained for a continuous spectrum of β-particles shall be the same as that obtained for the monokinetic electrons having an energy equal to the maximum energy of the β-spectrum.

Katz and Penfold have collected together the results of various workers relating to the paths of electrons in aluminium, for monokinetic electrons and for β-rays. The energy-path relationship so obtained is shown in Fig. 86. The characteristics of the curve are as follows:

$E < 2{\cdot}5$ Mev $\quad R = 412E^n$ (where $n = 1{\cdot}265 - 0{\cdot}094 \log E$)
$2{\cdot}5$ Mev $< E < 20$ Mev $\quad R = 530E - 106$

and here E is the energy expressed in Mev, and R is the path in mg./sq. cm.

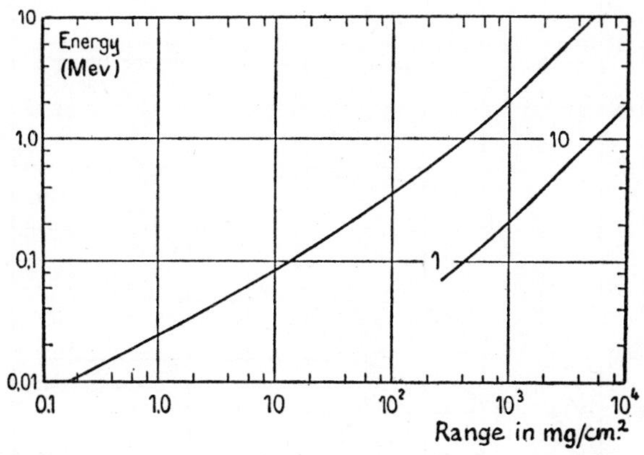

FIG. 86.—Energy-path relationship for electrons in aluminium.

There are very few results relating to other absorbents, but it seems that in the realm of energies corresponding to the figures given above, the track corresponding to a given energy (expressed in mass per unit area) is almost independent of the material used. At high emission energies, where braking action is important, few measurements have been made. The mean path might be estimated by integrating the calculated decelerating power. The following are some figures calculated by Heitler:

E . . .	0·5	5	50	500 Mev
Air	160	2×10^3	17×10^3	63×10^3 cm.
Water	0·19	2·6	19	78 cm.
Lead	$3{\cdot}7\times10^{-2}$	0·30	1·25	2·5 cm.

It will be noted that the braking effect is very important at high energies since in lead the particles of 500-Mev energy lose 450 Mev in the first 1·25 cm., and only 50 Mev in the subsequent 1·25 cm.

(10) Back-scattering

Another aspect of experimental importance, involving the behaviour of electrons, is back-scattering. If a thin source of β-rays is placed upon a thick support, a certain number of electrons emitted in the direction of this support undergo within this supporting medium sufficient scattering to cause them to retrace their path. As a result, the number of electrons emerging from the source in the direction forwards is more than 50 per cent of the total emission. This increase in intensity of electronic emission can become very considerable, and may be the cause of serious error in measurements. Fig. 87 shows

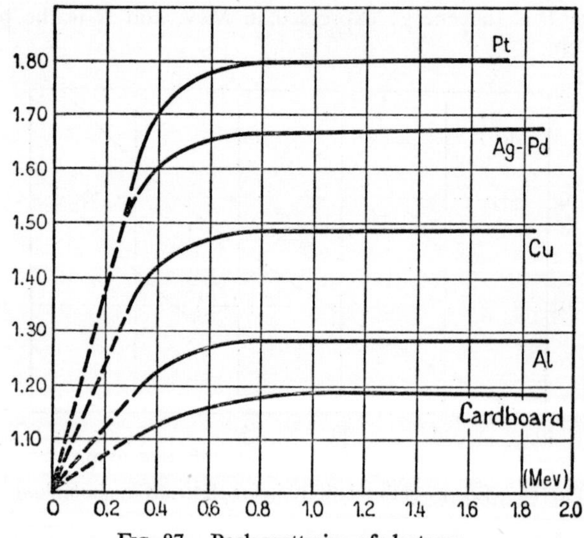

Fig. 87.—Back-scattering of electrons.

the increase in count rate in a G.M. counter placed in front of a β-emitter. The figures given are the ratios between counts for a very thick foil and a very thin one, and they are given for various energies of the β-rays, and also for several materials used for the supports. These curves are due to Burtt[29]. The effect reaches a maximum with a support consisting of a heavy medium, and reaches a high value, since the count rate may be increased by as much as 80 per cent.

(11) Annihilation of Positive Electrons

In most respects, the behaviour of positive and negative electrons is similar, but there is one important difference. The negative electron is a constituent particle of the atoms of matter, and when set in motion is likely to encounter only particles of its own kind, an encounter which does not result in its own annihilation. On the other hand, the positon, when in motion, meets only negatons, and during deceleration, or after complete deceleration, it becomes scattered within the medium according to the laws of thermal agitation, and finally undergoes annihilation together with a negaton which it has encountered.

Annihilation is a phenomenon which must conform to the conservation principles. The two charges, being of opposite sign and of the same absolute value, neutralize each other. The energy of the system is made up of the rest masses of the two particles together with the kinetic energy which the positon originally possessed. The quantity of motion is that of the positon, and will be zero if the positon was at rest at the moment of annihilation. Experiment has shown that this energy and this momentum are carried by the two photons formed at the moment of annihilation, or, in some special cases, by the three photons.

Dirac has calculated the effective cross-section of a negaton for annihilation with a positon of velocity $v = \beta c$. At non-relativistic velocities, the value of this is

$$\sigma = \frac{\pi r^2}{\beta} = \frac{2 \cdot 5 \times 10^{-25}}{\beta} \text{ sq. cm.}$$

It should be mentioned here that, since the effective section is inversely proportional to the velocity, the probability for annihilation in unit time $\sigma v n$, and the corresponding mean life

$$\tau = \frac{1}{\sigma v n} = \frac{1 \cdot 33 \times 10^{14}}{n},$$

are independent of velocity. In these expressions, n is the number of negatons per c.c. of the medium traversed by the positon. The most recent values of n are of the order of 10^{24} in condensed media, corresponding to a mean-life value of the order of 10^{-10} sec., which agrees with experimental results. The time necessary for a positon to lose its kinetic energy is somewhat lower than this value, and most positons are annihilated at the end of deceleration.

In such a case the energy to be dissipated is equal to $2mc^2$, and the annihilation radiation consists of a pair of photons of energy $mc^2 = 0 \cdot 511$ Mev, propagated in opposite directions.

In gases, n is about 1000 times smaller under normal conditions of temperature and pressure, and the mean life is of the order of 10^{-7} sec. Since the deceleration is also about 1000 times slower, the conclusions previously mentioned are still applicable.

Recent experimental work, especially that by Deutsch[30], has shown that while the preceding type of annihilation, in the case of gaseous media, conforms to a mean life which is inversely proportional to n, and hence to pressure, there are two other types of annihilation with periods independent of pressure, one very short ($\lesssim 10^{-10}$ sec.) and the other equal to 10^{-7} sec.

It has been shown that these two types of annihilation are characterized by the formation of a metastable system, the 'positonium atom', analogous to the hydrogen atom, but with the proton replaced by the positon. Such a system can exist in two different states according to the moments of rotation of the two electrons, depending whether these show parallel or antiparallel spin. In the second case, the mean life is very short and annihilation is accompanied by the emission of two photons. In the first case, the life is 10^{-7} sec., and three photons result from the annihilation. The relative importance of these two types of annihilation depends considerably on the nature of the gas used, but this dependence is at present little understood.

REFERENCES

1. CHEN, J. J. L., and WARSHAW, S. D. (1951), *Phys. Rev.*, **84**, 355.
2. GOLDWASSER, E. L., MILLS, F. E., and HANSON, A. O. (1952), *Phys. Rev.*, **88**, 1137.
3. WARNER, C., and ROHRLICH, F. (1954), *Phys. Rev.*, **93**, 406.
4. WILSON, W. (1911), *Proc. Roy. Soc.* A, **85**, 240.
5. BLOCH, S. (1912), *Ann. Phys. Lpz.*, **38**, 559.
6. TATE, J. T., and SMITH, P. T. (1932), *Phys. Rev.*, **39**, 270.
7. FROST, R. H., and NIELSEN, C. E. (1953), *Phys. Rev.*, **91**, 864.
8. MCCLURE, G. W. (1953), *Phys. Rev.*, **90**, 796.
9. STILLER, B., and SHAPIRO, M. M. (1953), *Phys. Rev.*, **92**, 735.
10. GROETZINGER, G., KEDER, L. B., RIBE, F. L., and BERGER, M. J. (1950), *Phys. Rev.*, **79**, 454.
11. PAGE, L. A. (1951), *Phys. Rev.* (1951), **81**, 1062.
12. BARBER, W. C., BECKER, G. E., and CHU, E. L. (1953), *Phys. Rev.*, **89**, 950.
13. SCOTT, M. B., HANSON, A. O., and LYMAN, E. M. (1951), *Phys. Rev.*, **84**, 638.
14. BEUCHNER, W. W., VAN DE GRAAFF, R. J., SPERDUTO, A., BURRILL Jr., E. A., and FESBACH, H. (1947), *Phys. Rev.*, **27**, 678.
15. LYMAN, E. M., HANSON, A. O., and SCOTT, M. B. (1951), *Phys. Rev.*, **84**, 626.
16. ANDRIEVSKY, KULCITSKY, and LATYSHEV (1943), *Sechenov J. Physiol.*, **6**, 279.
17. HANSON, A. O., LANZL, L. H., LYMAN, E. M., and SCOTT, M. B. (1951), *Phys. Rev.*, **84**, 626.
18. GOODRICH, M., LEVINGER, J. S., and PAYNE, W. (1953), *Phys. Rev.* (1953), **91**, 1225.
19. BUECHNER, W. W., VAN DE GRAAFF, R. J., BURRILL, E. A., and SPERDUTO, A. (1948), *Phys. Rev.*, **74**, 1348.
20. LANZL, L. H., and HANSON, A. O. (1951), *Phys. Rev.*, **83**, 959.
21. KOCH, H. W., and CARTER, R. E. (1950), *Phys. Rev.*, **77**, 165.
22. CURTIS, C. D. (1953), *Phys. Rev.*, **89**, 123.
23. FISHER, P. C. (1953), *Phys. Rev.*, **92**, 420.

24. De Wire, J. W., and Beach, A. L. (1951), *Phys. Rev.*, **83**, 476.
25. Schonland, B. F. J. (1923), *Proc. Roy. Soc.* A, **104**, 235; (1925), **108**, 187.
26. Chang, C. H., Cook, C. S., and Primakoff, H. (1953), *Phys. Rev.*, **90**, 544.
27. Tsin-San-Tsiang, Marty, C., and Dreyfus, B. (1947), *Journal de Physique*, **8**, 269.
28. Katz, L., and Penfold, A. S. (1952), *Rev. mod. Phys.*, **24**, 28.
29. Burtt, B. P. (1949), *Nucleonics*, **5**, 28.
30. A detailed account of the annihilation of positonium is to be found in an article by M. Deutsch, *Progr. Nucl. Phys.* (1953), **3**, 131.

Chapter 12

PHOTONS

(1) General

It is well known that photons are corpuscles associated with an electromagnetic field, and we need not go into the matter of their dual nature as corpuscular and undulatory entities. This duality actually applies to all particles that we have so far studied, but in these cases the undulatory nature of bodies with a rest mass which is not zero is not apparent unless a more profound study be made, and only becomes apparent when experiments such as electron diffraction are carried out.

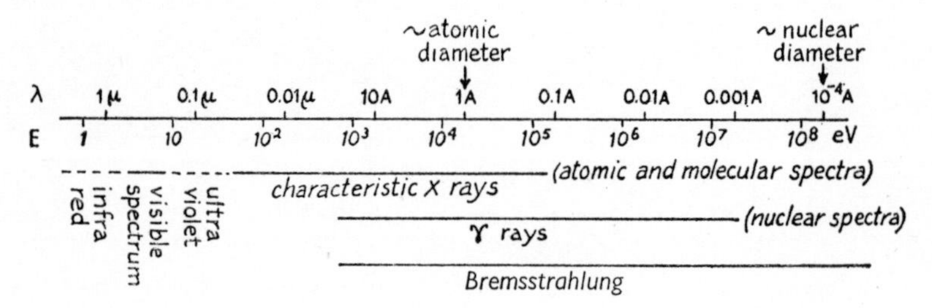

Fig. 88.—Energies and wavelengths of photons from various origins.

In the case of photons, the undulatory nature is, on the other hand, observable at very low energies (such as in the interference and diffraction of light), while at very high energies, such as may be encountered in nuclear physics, the corpuscular nature may tend to become of prime importance.

It will be recalled that the energy E of a photon is related to the frequency of the electromagnetic field by the proportionality relations $E = h\nu$, where h is the Planck's constant, or $6 \cdot 623 \times 10^{-27}$ c.g.s. units. From this, we obtain the relationship between the wavelength and the energy, i.e.

$$\lambda = \frac{\nu}{c} = \frac{ch}{E} \qquad \text{and} \qquad \lambda = \frac{1 \cdot 239 \times 10^{-4}}{E}$$

in which λ is expressed in cm. and E is in ev.

In increasing order of energies, or decreasing order of wavelengths photons belong to radiation categories which are distinguished by their mode of production and also by their properties. Fig. 88 represents these different groups schematically.

It should be mentioned here that whatever the terminology used, there is always, for a given energy, a definite particle, so that a photon of 50 kev will always have the same properties whatever the phenomenon which has given rise to it. The various terms used to describe them, such as characteristic X-rays, γ-rays, braking rays, and so on, emphasize this fact.

In what follows, we shall be concerned only with the photons associated directly or indirectly with nuclear phenomena, corresponding approximately with energies greater than 1 kev.

(2) Production of Photons by Braking

We may recall here that electrons in motion in a material medium can lose some of their energy by emission of photons during the course of braking action in the coulombic field of a nucleus. This phenomenon has been studied in connection with electrons, and need not now be reconsidered.

(3) Emission of γ-Rays

By γ-ray we mean a photon emitted during the course of nuclear transition from an excited state to one of smaller excitation, this latter being eventually the fundamental state.

We know that nuclei, like atoms, can exist only in definite energy states, of which the lowest is termed the 'fundamental'. The possible higher states of energy form a discontinuous series, characteristic of the particular nucleus, each term in the series being defined by its 'excitation energy', which is the excess of energy by which the state differs from the fundamental. The excited states of nuclei are generally unstable, and the nucleus tends to revert to the fundamental condition by the emission of energy in the form of photons. This de-excitation may take place in one stage, with the nucleus liberating all its energy of excitation as one photon, although a small correction has to be applied, as the nucleus takes a small part of the energy in the kinetic form in order to maintain the momentum of the system, or alternatively, the liberated energy may be given off in several stages, the nucleus passing through intermediate levels of excitation. In this latter case the energy is liberated in the form of several photons which are successively emitted. Most often, the nuclei in excited states have but short lives, too short, in fact, to be measurable by ordinary chronometric methods, and usually below 10^{-10} sec. However, sometimes the laws of forbidden states make the lives longer, and there may be metastable states involved. In fact, there are some nuclei known with lives of some months, but these are exceptional.

The formation of nuclei in excited states and giving rise to the emission of γ-rays by de-excitation, takes place essentially under two sets of circumstances. These are, respectively, the phenomenon of radioactivity, and the sequel to nuclear reactions.

In both cases the final nucleus may be formed in the fundamental state, but if energy available is sufficient, there may be formed excited states which will undergo de-excitation by photon emission.

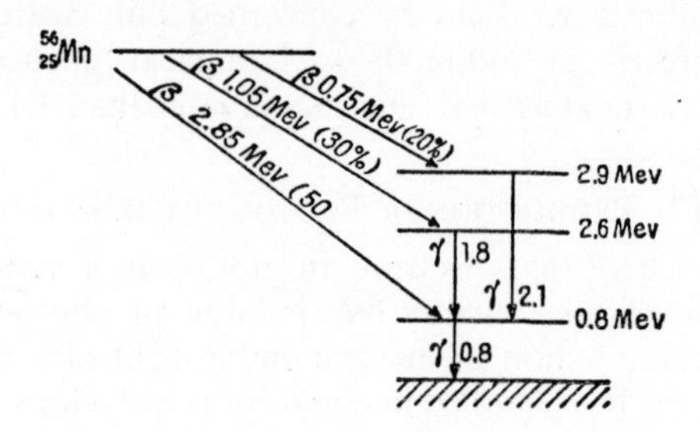

FIG. 89.—Radioactivity scheme for $^{56}_{25}$Mn.

Fig. 89 shows a scheme for the β-radioactivity of the nucleus of Mn-56, which gives rise to Fe-56, and this latter may occur in the form of three excited levels, the formation of the stable fundamental nucleus being impossible by laws of forbidden energy levels. The two highest energy levels are then de-excited by passing into the third level, with release of photons of 2·1 and 1·8 Mev energy

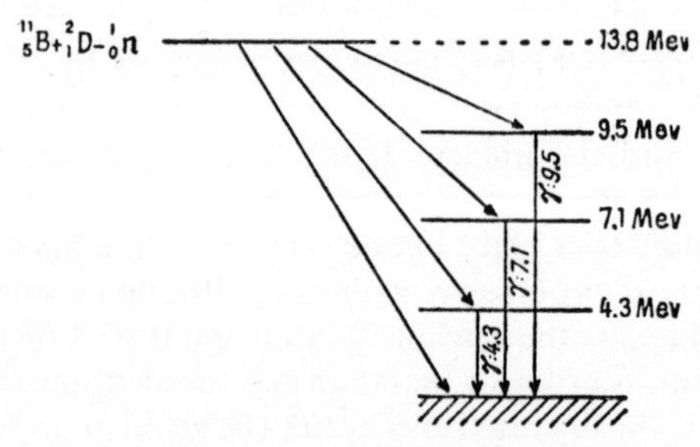

FIG. 90.—Scheme for nuclear reaction $^{11}_{5}B+^{2}_{1}D=^{12}_{6}C+^{1}_{0}n$.

respectively, and finally this third level reverts to the fundamental state by liberation of γ-photons of 0·8 Mev.

Fig. 90 shows a corresponding scheme for the nuclear reaction $^{11}_{5}B+^{2}_{1}D=^{12}_{6}C+^{1}_{0}n$. This reaction liberates 13·8 Mev, and if T is the kinetic energy of the incident deuteron, then the total energy is $T+13\cdot 8$ Mev, and after the reaction this has to be divided between the neutron and the carbon atom, the latter being in an excited state. Experiments show that the formation of three excited levels is involved, with energies of 4·3, 7·1, and 9·5 Mev respectively. These are then de-excited by emissions of photons of corresponding energies and formation of the fundamental state of the carbon atom.

(4) X-RAY EMISSION

We shall deal here only with the emission of X-rays following a nuclear reaction. Such rays are emitted whenever an electron from a strongly-bound level or shell has been displaced, and its place is taken by an electron from a less strongly-bound position. The increased energy of bonding thus involves emission of a photon.

Two nuclear phenomena can lead to the disappearance of a strongly-bound electron from the extra-nuclear shells.

The first of these is the electronic capture, a type of radioactivity in which the nucleus takes up one of the electrons which surround it, and naturally, this will involve the nearest levels, i.e. the K shell, and, to a smaller extent, the L shell. When the void left by the captured electron becomes re-filled, there is the emission of an X-photon.

The second is internal conversion. Photon emission is not the only method by which a nucleus can undergo de-excitation. It may equally well transfer its excitation energy to one of the electrons of the atom, expelling this electron from the level which it occupied, with an energy equal to the energy made available from the nucleus, decreased by the binding energy of the electron. This internal conversion applies almost solely to electrons in the most closely-bound electron levels, and the creating of a vacancy in such a shell is accompanied by the emission of X-rays.

(5) INTERACTION OF PHOTONS AND MATTER

If we neglect nuclear interactions of photons, which are produced less frequently than interactions of the electromagnetic type, we may distinguish three different phenomena which govern the behaviour of photons in matter: the photoelectric effect, the Compton effect, and the materialization effect.

(6) THE PHOTOELECTRIC EFFECT

Interaction is possible between a photon and an electron belonging to an atom, and the photon will vanish by giving up all its energy to that electron. This necessitates the possession by the electron of energy at least equal to the binding energy of the electron which is to be displaced.

The photoelectric effect cannot react with a free electron, as there are not then the conditions necessary for the two conservation principles. In fact, before interaction, the system consists of a photon of energy $h\nu$, and a quantum of movement $h\nu/c$ and an electron at rest. After interaction, the system consists of the electron with kinetic energy equal to $T=h\nu$, so that the energy is conserved.

In the case of a moving electron, the amount of movement of this would be

$$p = \frac{1}{c}\sqrt{\{T(T+2mc^2)\}}$$

which cannot be equal to $h\nu/c = T/c$.

On the other hand, if the electron is joined to an atom, the available kinetic energy is only $h\nu - E$, where E is the binding energy of the electron which becomes displaced. This kinetic energy will be divided between the electron and the remainder of the atom, and if both particles are in movement, it is always possible to satisfy the two conservation requirements. In practice, the atom is much heavier than the electron, so that a much smaller kinetic energy is sufficient in order to achieve a quantity of movement of the same order, neglecting the portion of energy which remains in the atom, and assuming that the electron carries off $h\nu - E$.

(7) Effective Atomic Section for the Photoelectric Effect

If a photon enters into interaction with one of the electrons of an atom, the photoelectric effect can only result with electrons which are bound with an energy smaller than the energy of the photon. Thus the effective cross-section in terms of photon energy will vary discontinuously as we pass from a value equal to the binding energy of one electron to that of another, and such discontinuity will reflect the increasing number of electrons in the atom susceptible to taking part in the photoelectric effect.

Fig. 91 shows, in the case of aluminium, copper, silver and lead, the variations in the mass absorption coefficient k in the energy region between 1 and 100 kev. It is related to the effective cross-section by the proportionality relationship $\sigma = kA/\boldsymbol{N}$, where A is the atomic mass of the material, and $\boldsymbol{N}$ the Avogadro number.

The curves show discontinuity as expected, and at the same time the two following characteristics become prominent:

(i) If we neglect the discontinuities, we see that the effective cross-section decreases as the photon energy increases, and this variation is approximately inversely proportional to the cube of the energy.

(ii) The effective section is an increasing function of Z, and approximately proportional to Z^3.

If we now consider energies greater than that at which the discontinuity for K absorption appears, we find that the effective cross-section varies regularly with energy and with Z. Much theoretical work has been done in order to obtain a formula which would express this regularity, but the complexity of the calculations has always been the reason for several approximations, and as a result no single formula is sufficient, but only a series of formulæ each of which is applicable over a limited range. Further, there have been

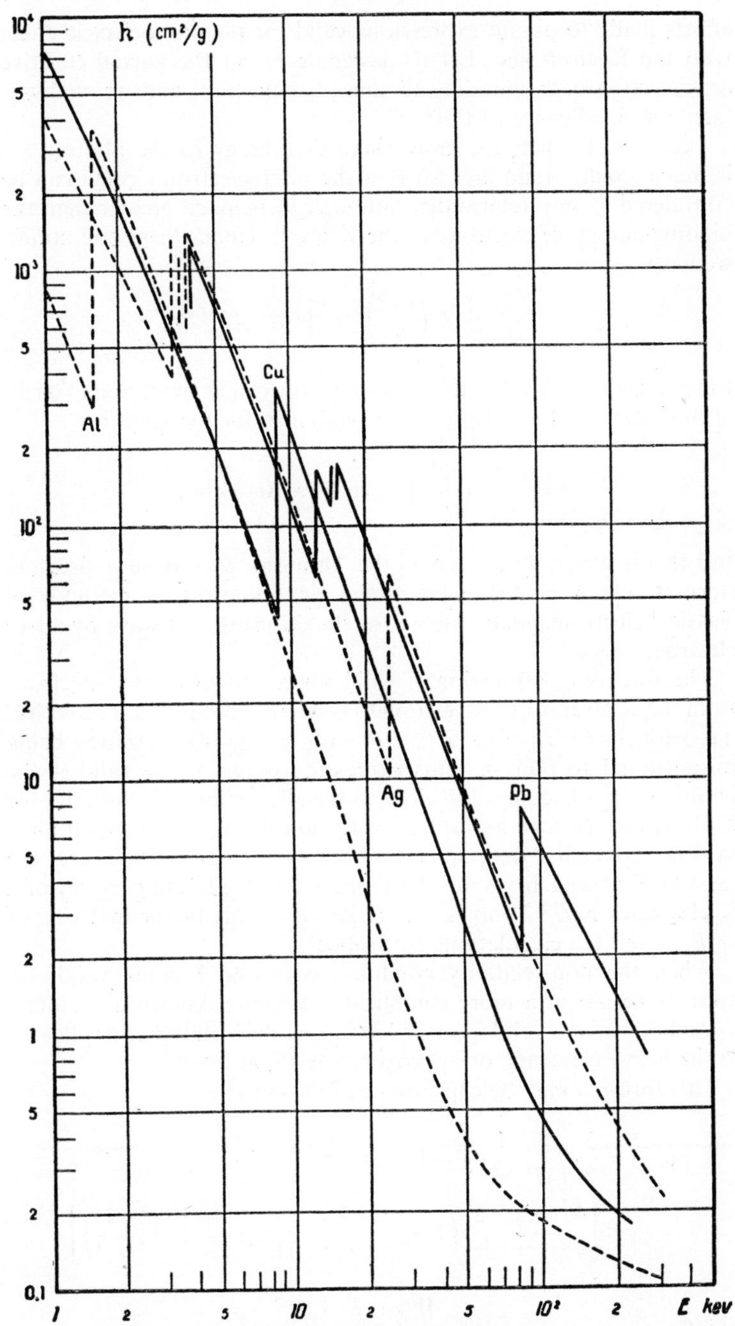

FIG. 91.—Absorption coefficient due to photoelectric effect in aluminium, copper, silver, and lead.

efforts made to obtain expressions valid for the photoelectric effect with the K electrons. Let us designate by σ_K the partial effective cross-section corresponding to this phenomenon, and we shall see later the significance of this.

Consider, further, the case where the energy of the photon, $h\nu$, is much smaller than mc^2, so that the photoelectron ejected can be considered as non-relativistic, although $h\nu$ is much greater than the binding energy of electrons in the K level. Under these conditions, we have

$$\sigma_K = \sigma_0 \cdot \frac{4\sqrt{2}}{137^2} \cdot Z^5 \left(\frac{mc^2}{h\nu}\right)^{\frac{7}{2}} = 1 \cdot 61 \times 10^{-8} . \sigma_0 \frac{Z^5}{\alpha^{\frac{7}{2}}},$$

where α is $h\nu/mc^2$ so that the photon energy can be expressed in terms of units mc^2, and we also use the symbol σ_0 for the quantity

$$\sigma_0 = \frac{8\pi}{3} \left(\frac{e^2}{mc^2}\right)^2 = 6 \cdot 65 \times 10^{-25} \text{ cm}^2,$$

and this is generally known as the Thomson effective cross-section since it represents the value found by Thomson by methods of classical electromagnetic theory for the diffusion of a wave by a free electron.

The foregoing expression is valid for a system of two electrons from the K level. It is interesting to observe the rapid change with Z (i.e. with the fifth power, Z^5), and with energy (the variation being proportional to $(h\nu)^{-\frac{7}{2}}$). This expression ceases to be valid if the photon energy becomes too close to the absorption discontinuity for K electrons. In such a case the expression for σ_K is to be multiplied by a factor smaller than unity, and becoming smaller the nearer the ratio $h\nu/E$ approaches unity, E_K representing the binding energy of a K electron. Fig. 92 shows the variation of this factor in terms of $h\nu/E_K$, from the calculations by Stobbe[1].

When the non-relativity condition ceases to become valid, we must make use of a more complicated formula, known as Sauter's formula[2], which is valid when $Z/137 \ll 1$, and which is thus applicable to the heavy elements, or approximately so, at least.

This formula may be expressed as follows:

$$\sigma_K = \sigma_0 \frac{3}{2} \cdot \frac{Z^5}{137^4} \cdot \frac{1}{\alpha^5} (\gamma^2 - 1)^{\frac{3}{2}}$$
$$\times \left[\frac{4}{3} + \frac{\gamma(\gamma-2)}{\gamma+1} \left(1 - \frac{1}{2\gamma\sqrt{(\gamma^2-1)}} \log \frac{\gamma + \sqrt{(\gamma^2-1)}}{\gamma - \sqrt{(\alpha^2-1)}}\right)\right],$$

where
$$\gamma = \frac{W_{el}}{mc^2} = \frac{h\nu + mc^2}{mc^2}.$$

This expression can take less complicated forms under extreme conditions, such as when

$$h\nu \ll mc^2, \qquad \gamma \simeq 1, \qquad \sigma_K = \sigma_0 \frac{4\sqrt{2}}{137^4} \cdot \frac{Z^5}{\alpha^{\frac{7}{2}}}$$

and

$$h\nu \gg mc^2, \qquad \gamma \gg 1, \qquad \sigma_K = \sigma_0 \frac{3}{2 \times 137^4} \cdot \frac{Z^5}{\alpha}.$$

This shows that the decrease with energy becomes less as the energy increases, since the power to which α is raised is being changed from

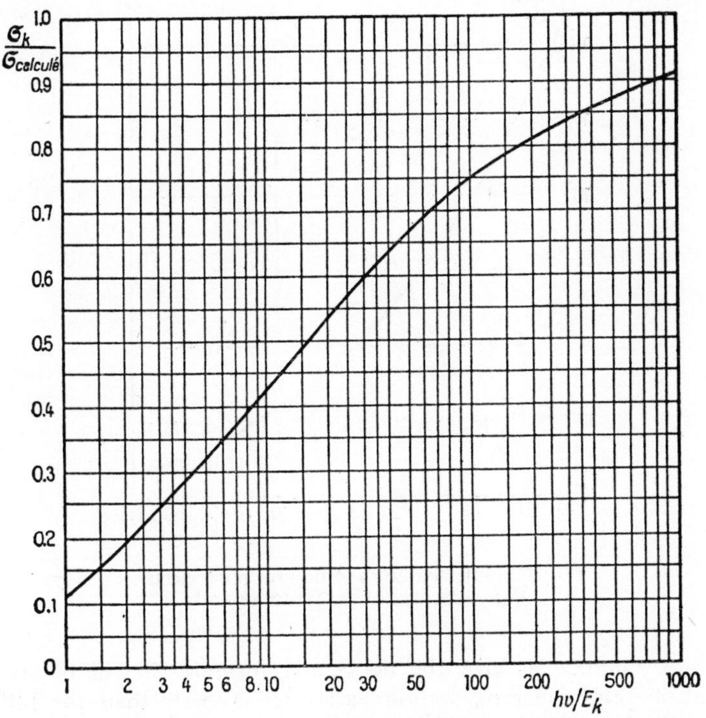

FIG. 92.—Stobbe correction for vicinity of K absorption discontinuity.

$\frac{7}{2}$ in the first case to unity in the second. The variation with Z remains proportional to Z^5 throughout, once we consider regions remote from the K discontinuities. Fig. 93 shows how α_K varies, according to the calculations of Sauter, the values being expressed in terms of units which are equal to

$$\frac{\sigma_0 Z^5}{137^4} = 1 \cdot 89 \times 10^{-35} Z^5 \text{ cm}^2.$$

The Sauter formula is limited to high Z values. Hall[3] has developed a formula which may be applied in cases of high energy, and this involves multiplication of the σ_K values previously used by a factor $e^{-\pi\xi+2\epsilon^2(1-\log\xi)}$, in which $\xi = Z/137$. At lower energies it is not necessary to make use of such corrections, but only of certain numerical values calculated by Hulme and his co-workers[4] for energies of 0·35 and 1·1 Mev. The table which follows shows values for Fe, Sn, and Pb, together with some values for elements of low

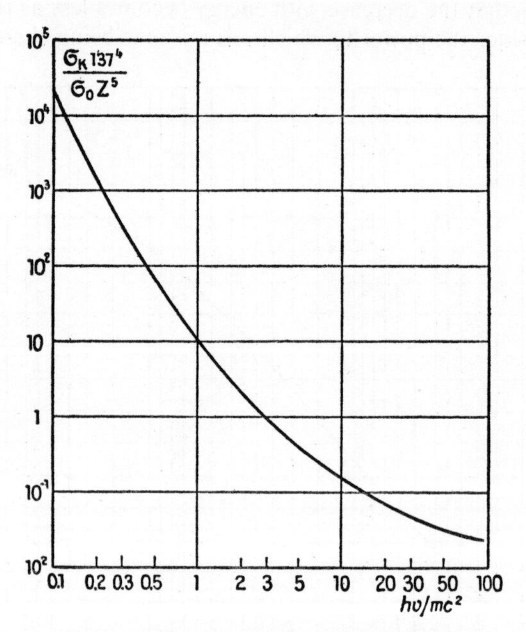

FIG. 93.—Effective cross-section for photoelectric effect according to the Sauter formula.

atomic number, as given by the Sauter formula. It will be seen that the effective cross-section varies less rapidly than the fifth power of Z. On the third line of the table are values of effective cross-sections valid only for high energies, derived by use of the Hall formula:

TABLE OF CALCULATED VALUES OF $\frac{\sigma_K . 137^4}{\sigma_0 . Z^5}$

α	small Z	Fe	Sn	Pb
0·69	43·6	27·0	18·3	11·8
2·2	1·70	1·58	1·20	0·90
very large	1·50/α	1·00/α	0·82/α	0·69/α

In Fig. 94 are collected the figures showing the variation of σ_K for various atoms, results previously mentioned having been taken into account.

The preceding results deal only with the photoelectric effect upon the two electrons of the K shell. The contribution of the other electrons has been much less studied. According to Hall, the contribution of the other electrons to the total effective cross-section of the atom is only $1/11 \cdot 2$, $1/9 \cdot 31$, $1/8 \cdot 49$, respectively, for iron, silver and tungsten in the region of the discontinuities for K absorption. At much higher energies, it tends towards $1/5$. The role of the K electrons is thus predominant, and the total effective section for the atom is often given as $(5/4)\sigma_K$.

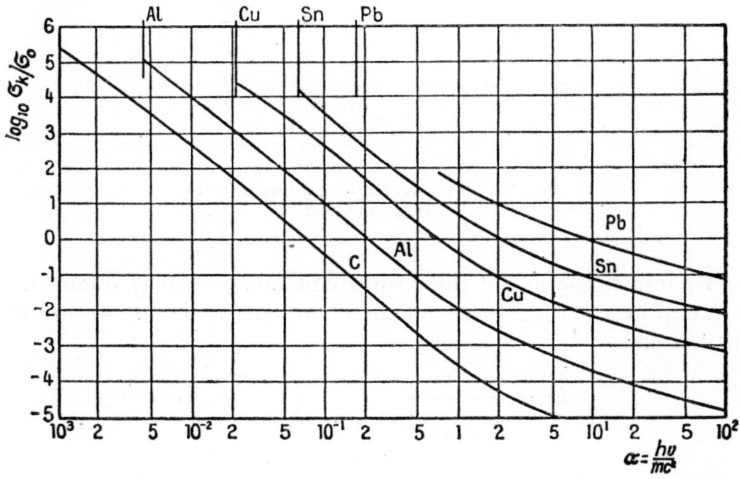

FIG. 94.—Variation of effective cross-section for photoelectric effect with energy.

Finally, we may say a word upon the direction of emission of photoelectrons. Theory and experience show that at low energies, i.e. when $\beta \ll 1$, the electrons are ejected mostly at right-angles to the direction of the incident beam of photons, but if we consider photons of energies such that $\beta \simeq 1$, their direction of emission approaches that of the propagation of the photon which ejected them.

(8) COMPTON EFFECT

The Compton effect is to be considered as an elastic impact of a photon against an electron. During such an impact, the photon transfers part of its energy to the electron which is struck, and as a result its wavelength is increased. It is easy to write equations of conservation for such an impact (Fig. 95). If we denote by ν_0 and ν the frequencies of the photon before and after the impact, and by

ϕ and θ the angle of deflection and the angle of projection of the photon-electron, then we have

$$h\nu_0 = h\nu - mc^2\left[\frac{1}{\sqrt{(1-\beta^2)}}-1\right],$$

$$\frac{h\nu_0}{c} = \frac{h\nu}{c}\cos\phi + \frac{m\beta c}{\sqrt{(1-\beta^2)}}\cos\theta,$$

$$0 = \frac{h\nu}{c}\sin\phi - \frac{m\beta c}{\sqrt{(1-\beta^2)}}\sin\theta.$$

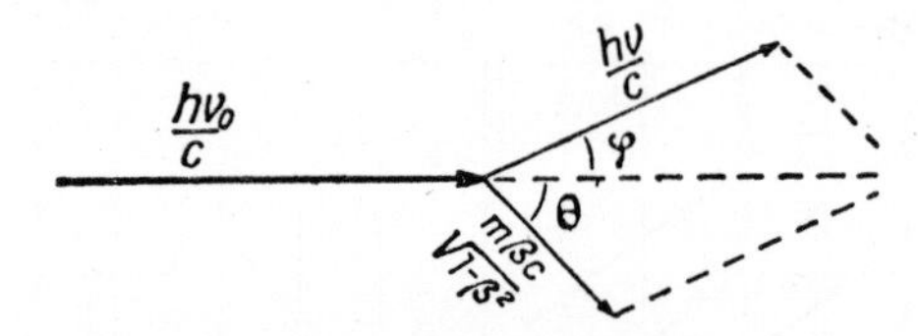

FIG. 95.—Conservation of impetus in the Compton effect.

By transformation of these three equations, we may obtain the relation between the energy of the photon after the impact and its deflection:

$$h\nu = \frac{h\nu_0}{1+2\alpha\sin^2\dfrac{\phi}{2}} \qquad \left(\alpha = \frac{h\nu_0}{mc^2}\right).$$

This relation indicates that, as ϕ varies from 0° to 180°, the energy of the photon decreases from the initial value $h\nu_0$ to its minimum value $h\nu_0/1+2\alpha$. When $h\nu_0$ is very large compared with mc^2, the diffused photons have an energy of $h\nu_0/2\alpha = mc^2/2$ independent of $h\nu_0$.

The variation of the wavelength is given by

$$\lambda = \lambda_0\left(1+2\alpha\sin^2\frac{\phi}{2}\right) = \lambda_0 + 2\Lambda\sin^2\frac{\phi}{2},$$

where $$\Lambda = \frac{h}{mc} = 2{\cdot}426\times 10^{-10} \text{ cm.},$$

being the wavelength of a photon of energy mc^2, and is called the Compton wavelength.

The wavelength of a photon diffused by the Compton effect increases to a maximum, diffusion being backwards, equal to two Compton wavelengths.

Naturally, since in the Compton effect the photon does not vanish and the two conservation relations can easily be satisfied, the effect may be produced equally well with free or bound electrons.

The theory of the Compton diffusion has been worked out by Klein and Nishina, and leads to the following formulæ in which the effective cross-section is always with respect to a single electron. In order to obtain the atomic effective cross-section, we must then multiply the values by Z.

The differential effective cross-section for the diffusion of an electron in the element of solid angle $d\Omega$, of which the mean direction makes an angle ϕ with the direction of propagation of the incident photon, is given by

$$d\sigma_\phi = \frac{3\sigma_0}{8\pi} d\Omega \frac{1+\cos^2\phi}{2} \cdot \frac{1}{\left[1+2\alpha\sin^2\frac{\phi}{2}\right]^2} \times \left[1+\frac{4\alpha^2\sin^4\frac{\phi}{2}}{(1+\cos^2\phi)\left(1+2\alpha\sin^2\frac{\phi}{2}\right)}\right].$$

The differential effective section for a photon of initial energy having after diffusion an energy between α and $\alpha+d\alpha$, is

$$d\sigma_\alpha = \tfrac{3}{8}\sigma_0 \frac{d\alpha}{\alpha_0^2}\left[\frac{\alpha_0}{\alpha}+\frac{\alpha}{\alpha_0}+\left(\frac{1}{\alpha}-\frac{1}{\alpha_0}\right)^2-2\left(\frac{1}{\alpha}-\frac{1}{\alpha_0}\right)\right].$$

The total effective section for the Compton effect, obtained by integration of one or other of the preceding formulæ, is

$$\sigma_c = \tfrac{3}{4}\sigma_0\left\{\frac{1+\alpha}{\alpha^3}\left[\frac{2\alpha(1+\alpha)}{1+2\alpha}-\log(1+2\alpha)\right]+\frac{1}{2\alpha}\log(1+2\alpha)-\frac{1+3\alpha}{(1+2\alpha)^2}\right\},$$

and this formula, in the two extreme cases, becomes:

non-relativistic: $\alpha \ll 1$ $\qquad \sigma_c = \sigma_0(1-2\gamma+\tfrac{26}{5}\gamma^2+\ldots)$,

extremely relativistic: $\alpha \gg 1$ $\qquad \sigma_c = \tfrac{3}{8}\sigma_0\frac{1}{\alpha_0}(\log 2\alpha_0+\tfrac{1}{2})$.

Fig. 96 shows the variation of σ_c with energy, and it can be seen that it is a decreasing function.

Also shown is the variation of effective cross-section for the photoelectric effect for various atoms divided by Z in order to obtain the value for single electrons, so that we may compare this with the effective section for the Compton effect. The decrease with energy is less rapid in the Compton effect than in the case of the photoelectric effect, and, for each element, there is an energy below which the photoelectric effect occurs, and above which the Compton effect preponderates.

As far as the direction of the emission of photoelectrons is concerned, we may work out relations for the correspondence law between θ and ϕ from the conservation relations

$$\cos\theta = (1+\alpha)\left(\frac{\sin^2\frac{\phi}{2}}{1+\alpha(\alpha+2)\sin^2\frac{\phi}{2}}\right)^{\frac{1}{2}},$$

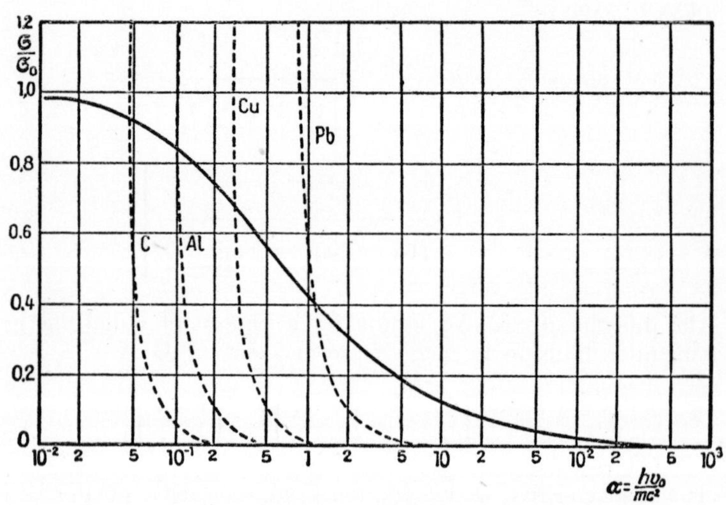

FIG. 96.—Variation with energy of effective section per electron for the Compton effect.

which shows that, as ϕ varies from 0° to 180°, θ varies from 90° to 0°. The law of the angular distribution of Compton electrons, which can be deduced from $d\sigma_\phi$, and the relationship between ϕ and θ, shows that these are emitted preferentially forwards, this preference being the more marked as α becomes larger.

(9) MATERIALIZATION EFFECT

The phenomenon of materialization consists of the formation of a pair of electrons, namely, a positon and a negaton, by the disappearance of a photon. If $h\nu$ is the energy of the photon, the conservation of the energy relationships means that

$$h\nu = 2mc^2 + T' + T'',$$

where $2mc^2$ represents the energy equivalent to the rest mass of two electrons formed, and T' and T'' are their kinetic energies. In fact, this is not rigorously correct, for materialization cannot occur outside the neighbourhood of a material mass, and the latter may participate in the phenomenon. Materialization occurring *in vacuo*, where the energy conservation would be represented by the equation given above, cannot satisfy the impulse conservation rule.

In fact, if $W' = mc^2 + T'$ and $W'' = mc^2 + T''$, the total energies of the two electrons

$$h\nu = W' + W''. \tag{i}$$

The momentum conservation also necessitates another equation,

$$\vec{h\nu} = \vec{cp'} + \vec{cp''}, \tag{ii}$$

where $\vec{p'}$ and $\vec{p''}$ are the quantities of movement of the two electrons connected with W' and W'' by the relationships

$$W' = \sqrt{(m^2c^4 + c^2p'^2)}, \qquad W'' = \sqrt{(m^2c^4 + c^2p''^2)}.$$

Condition (ii) also involves the condition

$$h\nu \leqslant cp' + cp'',$$

and even more so, $\quad h\nu < W' + W''$,

from which it is obvious that it is impossible to satisfy both equations (i) and (ii) simultaneously.

In practice, the materialization of photons is possible either in the coulombic field of a nucleus, or in that of an electron. Under these conditions, the nucleus or the electron taking part in the reaction, share in the energy, and the momentum also, so that equation (ii) may become rewritten in the form

$$\vec{h\nu} = \vec{cp'} + \vec{cp''} + \vec{cp'''}. \tag{iii}$$

However, at least in the case of the nucleus, which is much heavier than the electrons of the pair formed, the kinetic energy corresponding to the impulse $\vec{p'''}$ is negligible compared with that of the electrons, so that the relation for the energy conservation (i) can be considered as still valid.

Now let us consider the case of the materialization within the field of a nucleus. The theory of this event has been developed by Bethe and Heitler[5] within the limits of validity of the approximations imposed by Born, who says that $Z/137\beta$ should be $\ll 1$, where Z is the nuclear charge and β the velocity of the created electrons relative to that of light. Results will then be valid even for light nuclei and for high speeds of emission.

These workers have obtained a formula giving the effective cross-section for the possibility that a photon of energy $h\nu$ creates in the field of a nucleus of charge Ze an electron pair of which the positive particle has an energy lying between E and $E+dE$ (when $0 < E < h\nu - 2mc^2$). This formula will not be given here, for the analytical expression is quite complicated. By integration of the expression for all possible values of E, there results the total effective cross-section for the pair formation. Neglecting the screening effect of the electrons of the atoms, we find that this effective section is

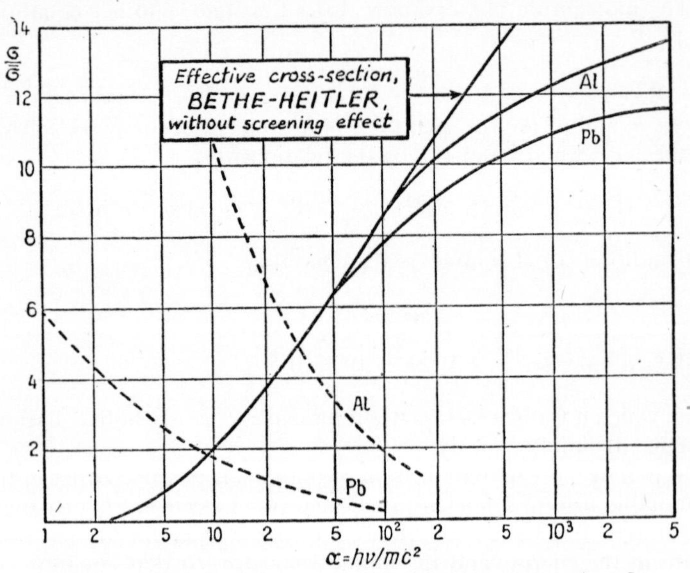

FIG. 97.—Variations with energy of the effective cross-sections for materialization of a photon in the field of a nucleus.

proportional to Z^2. Now taking, as is usual, as our unit for effective section the amount

$$\sigma = \frac{Z^2 r^2}{137} = Z^2 \times 5{\cdot}81 \times 10^{-28} \text{ cm}^2,$$

we obtain the law of the variation with energy which is valid for all nuclei and which is represented in schematic form in Fig. 97. If, on the other hand, we take into account the screening effect, which is not negligible at high energies, the effective section is decreased by an amount which increases as Z increases. Fig. 97 shows the curves corresponding to a light element (Al) and to a heavy element (Pb). The effective sections tend towards a limiting value at high energies, and this limiting value is given by

$$\sigma = \bar{\sigma}\left(\tfrac{28}{9}\log(183Z^{-\frac{1}{3}}) - \tfrac{2}{27}\right).$$

Naturally, the effective section becomes zero below $h\nu = 2mc^2$, which represents the threshold at which the photon fails to have enough energy to produce the mass of the two electrons. Equally, in contrast to the Compton effect and the photoelectric effect, the materialization has a cross-section which increases with energy. The result is that, for a certain characteristic energy for each element, there is an inversion of the order of importance relative to effective sections for the Compton effect and materialization. In Fig. 97 is given, expressed in the same units, the effective Compton section for Al and Pb (shown in broken lines), and it can be seen that this inversion occurs at energies which are respectively about 15 and 4 Mev.

As has been stated already, materialization of a photon can also take place in the field of an electron, but in this case the contribution of the latter to the energy partition is far from negligible, and after materialization the kinetic energy is distributed between three particles, i.e., the two electrons which have been formed, and the electron in the field of which the phenomenon has taken place. This group is known as the 'triplet'.

It can be shown that the threshold of the phenomenon is no longer $2mc^2$, but $4mc^2$, because of the small mass of the electron, which makes it impossible to satisfy simultaneously the two conservation principles unless the photon has at least this energy. The effective cross-section for the system of electrons is, on the whole, proportional to their number, i.e. Z, while that of the nucleus is Z^2. Thus, one obtains the total effective section by replacing, in the formula for $\bar{\sigma}$, Z^2 by $Z(Z+A)$, where A is a number of the order of unity, and which tends towards zero as $h\nu$ decreases towards $4mc^2$. It does not appear that these results, nor the experimental results, are accurate enough to enable us to say more.

It has already been stated that the results given must be used with caution, when heavy elements and feeble energies are involved. Calculations show, when applied to certain cases, some idea of the degree of approximation involved. Thus, Hulme and Jaeger[6] have calculated that, in the case of photons of 1·5 and 2·6 Mev, the effective section for lead is $0{\cdot}17\bar{\sigma}$ and $0{\cdot}73\bar{\sigma}$, while the Bethe-Heitler formula gives $0{\cdot}08\bar{\sigma}$ and $0{\cdot}67\bar{\sigma}$, so that there is an error factor of 2 in the first case, but only 10 per cent in the second.

The Bethe-Heitler formula enables us to forecast the law of distribution of the total kinetic energy between the two particles which have been formed. In the approximations involved in this formula, the two electrons play an equal rôle, symmetrically. If x is the fraction of the available kinetic energy carried off by one of the electrons—the positon, for example—the differential cross-section is given by

$$d\sigma_+ = f(x)\,dx,$$

this being the section for the positon having an energy lying between x and $x+dx$.

Fig. 98 shows the function $f(x)$ for various values of the energy of the photon, and it will be noted that at energies below a few Mev, the probability reaches a maximum for equal partition between the two electrons, while at high energies, on the other hand, such a partition corresponds to a minimum, while the maximum probability

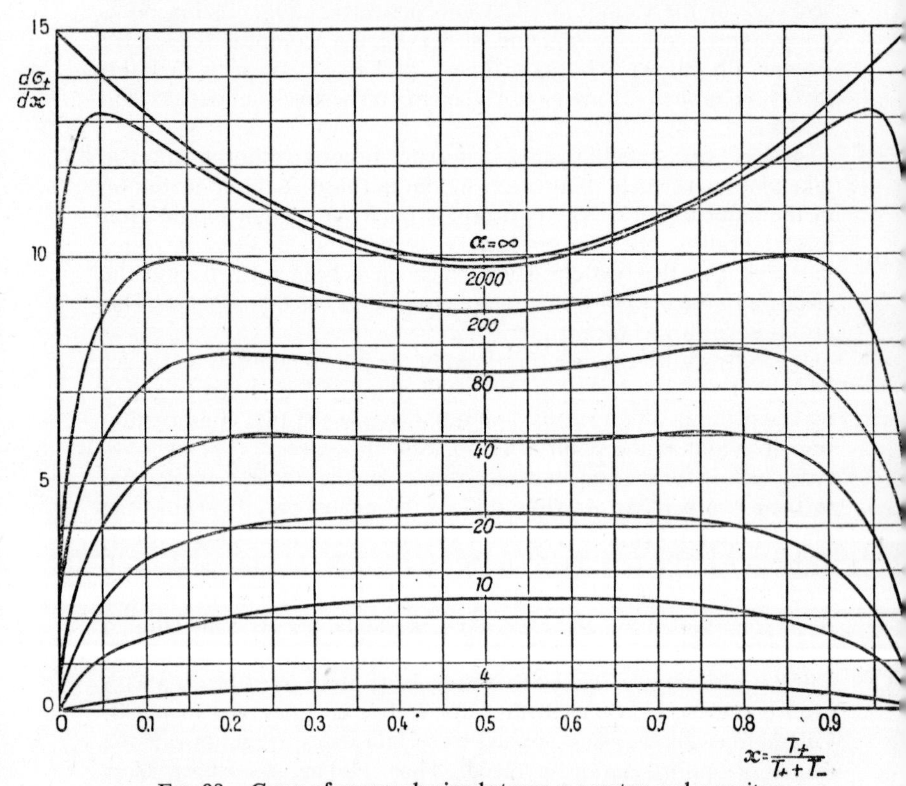

FIG. 98.—Curve of energy-sharing between a negaton and a positon.

corresponds to the case in which one of the electrons carries off almost all the available energy, the other particle receiving almost none.

In reality, the action of the coulombic field of the nucleus on the created electrons tends to repel the positon and to hold back the negaton, so that a correction should be introduced in order to take this fact into account. This correction would make the curves of Fig. 98 asymmetrical, and give, on the average, a larger kinetic energy to the positon than to the negaton. There appears to be no precise data available on this correction. Hulme and Jaeger have made the calculation in the case of lead, for energies of $h\nu = 1 \cdot 5$ and $2 \cdot 6$ Mev, and have found the mean values of the energy ratios $\bar{T}_{+}/\bar{T}_{-}$ to be $2 \cdot 0$ and $1 \cdot 4$ respectively.

(10) Relative Importance of Various Phenomena

The scheme given here indicates in the case of Al, Cu, and Pb, which can be considered as representatives of materials of low Z, medium Z, and high Z, the regions of energies where the various phenomena are predominant. In this scheme, P indicates the photoelectric effect, C the Compton effect, and M materialization.

		50	150	500	kev	5	10	15	Mev
Al	P				C				M
Cu		P			C				M
Pb		P			C			M	

(11) Cascade Showers

When a photon of very high energy penetrates a material medium, the probability that the first phenomenon produced will be a materialization is almost unity. The electrons so formed have very high energies themselves, and as a result their deceleration will give rise to emission of photons by the braking effect, and these photons will now give rise to electron pairs by materialization, and so on. The phenomenon results in a multiplication of particles including photons and electrons of both signs, between which the originally available energy will be distributed. The multiplication comes to an end when the energy of the photons has become too low for pair production, or when the energy of the electrons formed has reached a value below the critical energy.

It is clear that the cascade shower can be started off quite equally well by a photon or an electron, the only criterion being that there is sufficient energy available at the commencement of the process. The phenomenon has been observed to start from photons and from electrons in the cosmic rays, but since the availability of particle accelerators, the energies of which can reach hundreds of Mev at present, such cascades have been also observable in the laboratory.

The distance over which such a cascade can develop is determined by the mean free path of the photons before the creation of an electron pair, and the mean free path of the electron before emission of the Bremsstrahlung photons. These two values are of the order of magnitude which we called radiation length when talking of electrons. One can say, then, very approximately, that the development of a cascade occurs over several radiation lengths.

(12) Photon Absorption

Of the three phenomena already considered, two involve the disappearance of the photon, while the third involves simply a decrease of energy, accompanied by a change in direction. Thus when we talk of the absorption of a photon, we must specify whether the photon has suffered Compton diffusion and is absorbed or not.

In order to define the magnitude which we call the absorption coefficient we assume photons to be absorbed when they undergo any interaction. Consider the apparatus shown in Fig. 99. The photons are in a monokinetic beam emitted from a source S, and are

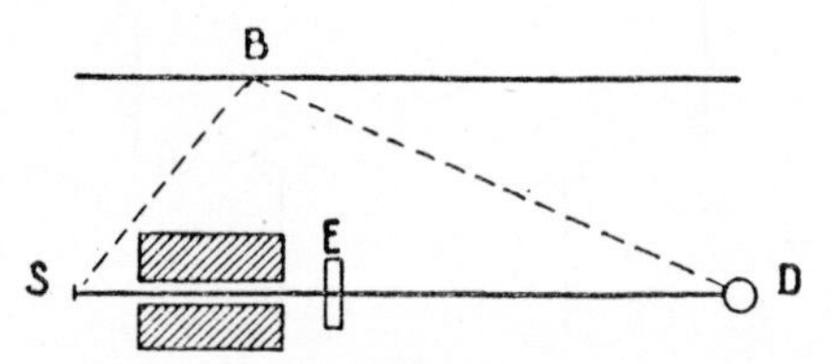

Fig. 99.—Apparatus for measuring photon absorption.

stopped by the absorbing foil, usually of lead, pierced with a small hole so as to allow the passage only of those photons having a direction parallel with the axis of propagation. The detector D (which may be a G.M. counter, scintillation apparatus, etc.) gives a response which is proportional to the number of photons in the beam. If now we interpose into the path of the beam the screen E, a number of photoelectric events will be produced, accompanied by materialization, so that photons vanish, while some Compton phenomena occur and lead to photons passing through the metal screen and then suffering capture within the detection apparatus. Suppose that σ_p, σ_c, and σ_m are the effective sections of the foil atoms relative to the three effects for photons of the energy considered. The effective total absorption section will then be

$$\sigma = \sigma_p + \sigma_c + \sigma_m,$$

and the number of photons remaining after passage through the foil of thickness x will be

$$N = N_0 e^{-n\sigma x} = N_0 e^{-\mu x},$$

where N_0 is the number of incident photons and n the number of atoms per c.c. of the foil material.

The quantity $\mu = n\sigma$ is called the absorption coefficient of the substance forming the foil, and relating to photons of the given energy.

Fig. 100 shows the variation of μ as a function of the photon energy for aluminium, copper, and lead. The existence of a minimum for μ is associated with the fact that σ_p and σ_c decrease with energy while σ_m increases. On the graph is also shown the thickness (right-hand

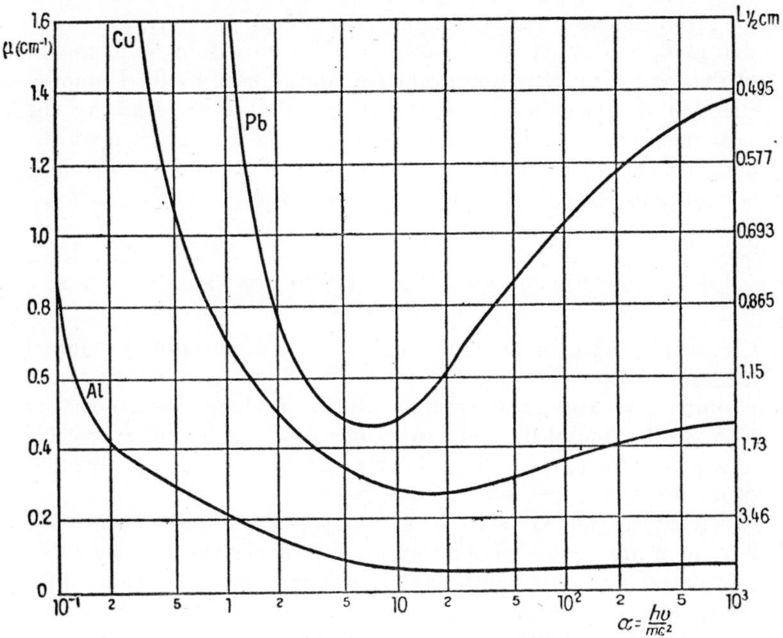

FIG. 100.—Variation with energy of absorption coefficient of photons in aluminium, copper, and lead.

scale) corresponding to half-absorption $= L_{\frac{1}{2}} = 0 \cdot 693/\mu$. The energy at which this minimum occurs, i.e. when the photons have their greatest penetrating power, is lowest when Z is largest. Here are a few values:

Be	C	N	O	Al	Fe	Cd	W	Pb	U
94	56	46	39	21	9	4·4	3·5	3·4	3·3 Mev

For purposes of orientation of ideas, it should be remembered that 1·5 cm. of lead, which is an absorber frequently in use, will stop one-half of the photons of greatest penetrating power. Thus, 15 cm. will produce an intensity of $(\frac{1}{2})^{10} \sim \frac{1}{1000}$, while with 30 cm. the intensity is $(\frac{1}{2})^{20} \sim 10^{-6}$.

In many practical cases these ideal conditions shown in Fig. 99 are not realized. This is the case, for example, when we study the penetration of photons into a medium which extends in three directions, from the entry face. We must then take into account the photons which are diffused by the Compton effect which are also deviated from the original direction and with loss of energy. Such a problem is obviously complex and cannot be considered here.

Even in the case of the set-up in Fig. 99, care must be taken with the arrangement of the apparatus. A very frequent cause of error is that photons emitted by the source in a direction different from that of the canal or perforation in the foil are diffused by the Compton effect in the neighbouring material, or even in the walls of the experimenting room (path SBD), and then have an effect upon the detector D. Thus, if the measurements are to make sense, it is necessary to place the foils in such a way as to prevent such effects.

(13) Equilibrium Between Radiated Photons and Secondary Electrons

Consider a beam of photons of energy $h\nu$, penetrating a material medium, normal to the surface of entry. After penetration, certain photons give rise to interaction which produces movements of electrons by one of the three usual methods. It should be possible to work out the proportion of electrons put into motion as a function of the depth of penetration of the photons.

A complete calculation of this phenomenon would be very difficult, but there are certain simplifications in calculation which may be introduced, and although these do not approximate to reality, they at least allow us to obtain a resulting calculation of which the essential characters are not too remote from reality.

We suppose that every interaction of a photon corresponds to the emission of an electron in the direction of propagation of the photon and that this electron travels in a rectilinear trajectory of very definite length R.

We now seek the number of secondary electrons formed at a depth a, which is smaller than R. These are the secondary electrons emitted between the surface of entry where $x = 0$, and the surface where $x = a$. If N represents the number of entry photons and μ their absorption coefficient, there will be left of them a proportion $Ne^{-\mu x}$ at distance x, and between x and $x + dx$ there will be formed $Ne^{-\mu x}\mu\,dx$ secondaries. Thus, at a depth a there will be a total of

$$n_s = \int_0^a Ne^{-\mu x}\mu\,dx = -N(1 - e^{-\mu a})$$

secondary electrons.

Now consider the depth $a > R$, where only those secondary electrons formed between a and $a-R$ are to be found. These will number

$$n_s = \int_{a-R}^{a} N e^{-\mu x} \mu \, dx = N(e^{\mu R} - 1) e^{-\mu a}.$$

From Fig. 101 (*a*) it will be seen that the number of secondary electrons increases up to a depth $a = R$, and then decreases exponentially with the absorption coefficient of the photons. Further, there is a constant relationship between the number of secondary electrons and the number of photons. The photons are said to be in equilibrium with the secondary electrons which they produce.

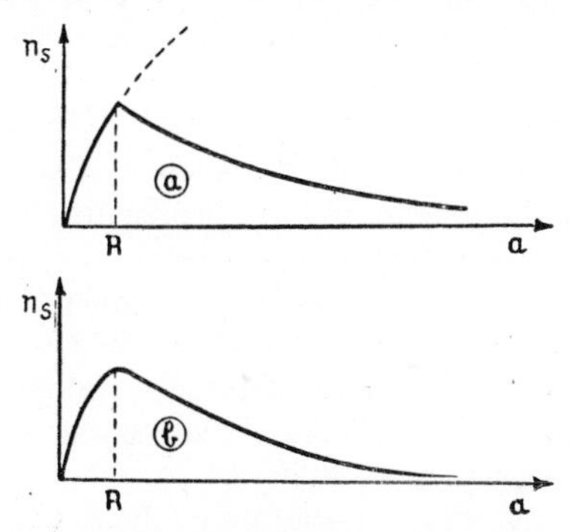

FIG. 101.—Establishment of equilibrium between photons and their secondaries: (*a*) simplified theoretical case; (*b*) practical trend of phenomenon.

In practice, the simplifying hypotheses introduced into the calculations are not realized. Nevertheless, the preceding results remain qualitatively valid. The number of secondary electrons increases from zero to the maximum obtained at a depth of penetration of the order of the range of the secondaries, and then decreases exponentially with the absorption coefficient of the photons such that the number of secondaries is related to that of the photons in a constant way (Fig. 101 (*b*)).

These considerations are important when we wish to design photon detection devices based upon the properties of the secondaries. For example, this is utilized in the detection of photons by the Geiger counter. The efficiency becomes greater the greater the number of secondaries extracted from the walls of the counter, and the latter must have a thickness of the order of the range of the secondaries in the wall material. Many workers have measured the efficiency of Geiger counters having this optimum wall thickness.

Here are some numerical values for various energies and various wall thicknesses:

$h\nu$ =	0·25	0·5	1	2	4	Mev
Al =	0·8	4·0	8·0	14	24	per 1000
Cu =	1·8	3·2	6·3	14	25	,, ,,
Au =	15·0	10·0	9·0	13	24	,, ,,

It will be seen that these efficiencies, which represent simply the ratios of numbers of secondaries extracted from the walls of the detector to the number of photons, are always very low, being of the same order of magnitude for various metals at energies of 1 Mev or more, but higher in the case of heavy metals at energies of less than 1 Mev.

(14) Definition of Radiation at a Point

Consider an element of volume dv in air and surrounding a point A in a region in which photons are propagated in a direction and with an energy which need not be specified. During the observation time T a certain number of ionizing secondary electrons will be produced in dv as a result of interactions of the photons with the gaseous atoms in the air. Each of these secondaries is propagated over a certain distance, and creates within the zone around dv a number of ion-pairs which we shall call $I dv$. The symbol I may now be defined as the quantity of radiation or the radiation dose received at point A during the time T. Such a dose may be measured not only by the number of ion-pairs created, but also in röntgens, the röntgen being the radiation dose for which the secondary electrons formed in 1 c.c. of air give rise to $2 \cdot 08 \times 10^9$ ion-pairs. This number is simply defined as the number of ion-pairs forming 1 electrostatic unit of charge of ions of each sign.

It is clear that this definition is essentially a measure of the ionization by the secondaries and that it is not equivalent to a definition of the beam of primary photons. It is, however, extremely useful when applied to the study of effects produced by photons directly related to the ionization produced by their secondaries, and in biological effects in particular.

The problems of measurement of a dose in röntgens is not easy, and cannot always be satisfactorily carried out. Fortunately, in practice, we may usually replace the measurement of the dose at a point by that of the ionization produced in 1 c.c. of air around that point.

According to definition, the two quantities are not necessarily equal, and we must seek conditions under which they will become so, taking into consideration the case in which we have a monoenergetic photon beam propagated in a parallel fashion in a given direction.

In most practical cases, the beams are more or less of this type, or can be considered as superpositions of such beams differing only in energy or in direction of propagation.

The secondaries are to be considered as formed within an element of volume around the point A, and giving rise to secondaries which ionize the air in a sphere of radius R with its centre at A, where R is the maximum range of these secondaries. Now consider the ionization produced in the unit volume around the point B (Fig. 102). Clearly, this is equal to the ionization created in the unit volume around point A by the secondaries which were formed in the volume around B′ which is related symmetrically to A in the same way as B is, provided the photon density is the same at B′ as at B, and at A. Since the same argument can be applied to all points in space, it may

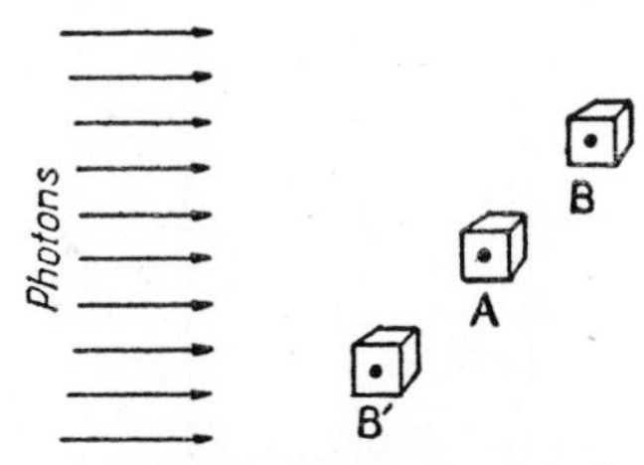

FIG. 102.—Equivalence of ionization produced in B by secondaries issuing from A, and formed in A by secondaries issuing from B′.

be seen that: if the photon flux is uniform within a circular section of radius R perpendicular to the direction of propagation, and if the absorption of the photon beam is negligible over the distance $2R$, then the number of ion-pairs created in 1 c.c. around A will be a measure of the radiation at that point. This last condition is particularly favourably fulfilled at low energies, and may be expressed in the form $2R \ll L_{\frac{1}{2}}$, if $L_{\frac{1}{2}}$ is the absorption half-length for the photons.

Thus the problem becomes one of ionization around a point, and the ionization chamber now comes into its own. Unfortunately the walls of such an instrument introduce errors by giving rise to emission of secondary electrons which falsify the measurement.

This difficulty, however, may be overcome in the following way. Instead of considering a certain volume of air at ordinary pressure, we take into consideration a medium which simulates air at very high pressure, i.e. some solid medium formed of atoms of atomic number close to that of air. Graphite is usually employed, while more complex materials such as bakelite may also be used. The linear dimensions of the block must be small compared with the absorption half-length for the photons in the medium, in order that no appreciable change will be produced in the intensity of the photon beam, and yet greater than the range of the secondaries in the same medium, so that in the centre the photons and their secondaries may be considered as in equilibrium (Fig. 103).

If ρ is the ratio of the densities of the medium and normal air, then the number of ion-pairs per unit volume of the medium at the centre of the block is equal to ρI, where I is the number of ion-pairs which would be formed in normal air. In order to measure ρI, a cavity is provided in the block, the dimensions of which are much less than the range of the secondaries, and this cavity is then used like an air-filled ionization chamber. Such a cavity does not appreciably change the distribution of the photons and their secondaries,

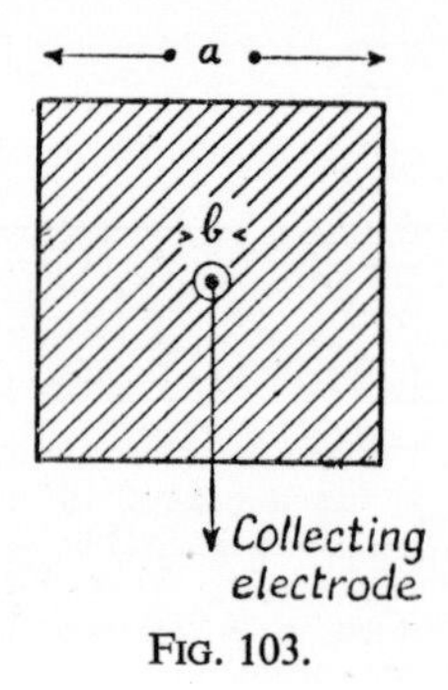

FIG. 103.

and the ionization formed therein is ρ times smaller than that which would have resulted had the cavity been filled in. As a result, if v is the volume of the cavity, the measured ionization is Iv.

Summarizing, we may now state that the measured ionization will be a measure of the amount of radiation if

$$b \ll 2R < a \ll L_{\frac{1}{2}},$$

where a, b are the external linear dimensions and internal linear dimensions of the ionization chamber, R the maximum range of the secondaries in the wall material, and $L_{\frac{1}{2}}$ the half-absorption length for the photons in the wall material.

Such a condition may be satisfied if $R \ll L_{\frac{1}{2}}$, and, in fact, this is possible for photon energies below some 10 Mev. At higher energies, R tends to become of the same order as or even greater than $L_{\frac{1}{2}}$, and although the condition $b \ll 2R < a$ may be still true, since $a \ll L_{\frac{1}{2}}$ will no longer apply, we must calculate the correction to be applied so that we may take into account the absorption of photons in the walls of the chamber.

In practice, use is often made of ionization chambers which do not conform to these conditions, but which may be calibrated by comparison with a standard chamber. Such pieces of apparatus must be used with caution since their calibration is likely to depend upon the energy of the photons, and they tend to give only the order of magnitude of the quantity of radiation.

The use of the röntgen measurement of photon radiations has been much developed over the last few years as a result of the extended use of apparatus giving intense sources of X-rays or γ-rays (such as accelerators and piles). Users of such apparatus need to be protected against their damaging action, and 0·3 röntgen per week has been accepted as the maximum weekly dose of radiation which may be taken by an individual.

For comparison, it should be remembered that at a distance of 1 m., 1 g. of radium gives an intensity of radiation of 1 röntgen per hour. In such an environment a person must remain for not longer than 20 minutes per week.

Finally, mention should be made of the difficulties which arise from the complexity of the definition of the röntgen, and from its use, and as a result biologists have come to use as their unit of radiation the rad, which is a unit of absorbed dose. When a material is submitted to irradiation by photons, there is transfer of energy, by way of the secondary electrons formed. The absorbed dose is 1 rad when the energy transferred by the photons to the medium is 100 ergs per g. Unfortunately, this unit is not always applicable, since there is no very accurate method of measuring the energy liberated in the medium, especially a medium as complex as biological tissue.

REFERENCES

1. STOBBE, M. (1930), *Ann. Phys. Lpz.*, **7**, 661.
2. SAUTER, F. (1931), *Ann. Phys. Lpz.*, **11**, 454.
3. HALL, H. (1936), *Rev. Mod. Phys.*, **8**, 358.
4. HULME, H. R., MCDONGALL, J., BUCKINGHAM, R. A., and FOWLER, R. H. (1935), *Proc. Roy. Soc.* A, **149**, 131.
5. BETHE, H. A., and HEITLER, W. (1934), *Proc. Roy. Soc.* A, **146**, 83.
6. HULME, J. C., and JAEGER, H. R. (1935), *Proc. Roy. Soc.* A, **153**, 443.

NAME INDEX

SUBJECT INDEX